C000101667

The Power of...
HERBS

The Power of...
HERBS

Origins • Traditions • Facts & Flavours

Gill Davies

WORTH
PRESS

First published in 2015
by Worth Press Ltd, Cambridge, England.
info@worthpress.co.uk

© Worth Press Ltd, 2015

Text © Gill Davies
The author has asserted her rights under the Copyright, Designs and Patents Act 1988
to be identified as the author of this work.

British Library Cataloguing in Publication Data. A catalogue record for this book is
available from the British Library.

ISBN: 978-1-84931-091-8

10 9 8 7 6 5 4 3 2 1

Publisher's Note: While every effort has been made to ensure that the information
herein is complete and accurate, the publisher and author make no representations
or warranties either expressed or implied of any kind with respect to this book to the
reader. Neither the author nor the publisher shall be liable or responsible for any
damage, loss or expense of any kind arising out of information contained in this book.
The thoughts or opinions expressed in this book represent the personal views of the
author and not necessarily those of the publisher. Further, the publisher takes no
responsibility for third party websites or their content.

The Power of Herbs contains information on a wide range of herbs that can be used in
cooking as well as being taken medicinally. It is not intended as a medical reference
book and the mention of the benefits particular to a herb are for information only.
Before trying any herbal remedies it is strongly suggested that a GP or other medical
professional be consulted first. It is important to remember that some herbs that
are beneficial in small doses can be harmful if taken in greater quantities or for an
extended period of time. These herbs are clearly marked on the page by this symbol
in red: △. There is space here for only very brief descriptions of the medicinal uses of
herbs but more details of botanical medicine, both present and ancient herbal cures,
are readily available in specialist books or websites. Neither the author nor the publisher
can be held responsible for any adverse or allergic reactions to the suggestions or
information contained within this book and the use of any herb or its derivatives is
actioned completely at the reader's own risk.

The images used in this book come from either the public domain or from the public
commons unless otherwise stated.

Design and layout: Arati Devasher, www.aratidevasher.com
Editor: Meredith MacArdle
Picture research: Meredith MacArdle, Arati Devasher

Printed and bound in China

CONTENTS

Introduction   8

Discovering the Herbs   **15**
Popular Culinary Herbs   17
Floral Healing Herbs   53
Medicinal Herbs   117

Fascinating Facts   153
Powerful Herbs: Cancer Treatments   167
Herbs Across the World: 173
  National Herbs, State Symbols and Popular Herbs
Sense and Emotions: 179
  The Language of Herbs and Flowers

Index   190
Image Credits   191
Acknowledgements and Bibliography   192

POISONOUS OR TOXIC HERBS

Look out for this sign, indicating toxic or poisonous herbs.

KEY TO SYMBOLS

 VARIETIES OF HERBS

 TRADITIONALLY USED FOR

 POISONS AND TOXINS

 OILS AND REMEDIES

 DID YOU KNOW?

 FAIRY TALES

INTRODUCTION

It was way back in 1,500 BC that the use of herbs as medicines was first noted in one of the oldest preserved medical records known, named the Ebers Papyrus after its discoverer, Georg Ebers, who spotted the document in an Egyptian market in in 1872. Undoubtedly herbs were being used long before this official report and throughout the centuries have been a powerful element in diet, medicine and magic. They have been used to flavour food, make perfumes, as ingredients for potions and spells and to serve countless medical and spiritual needs.

The word herb derives from the old French *erbe* meaning grass or plant: the 'h' did not appear until in the 1400s and remained silent until the 1800s (Americans still have a silent 'h'). Although any part of the plant might be considered for herbal *medicine* – flowers, leaves, roots, seeds, berries, resin or bark – in *culinary* use, only the leafy green parts are classed as herbal. Other portions serve as spices.

Herbs stir the taste, invigorate the senses and have long been associated with medication, cures and wellbeing. Today they are used to add flavour, boost health and as an alternative medicine (any plant with *officinalis* in its Latin name can be used as a medicine). We may now

Meadowsweet

Picked and cut herbs, ready to add flavour and savour to dishes.

pluck them from the supermarket shelf or a window box – rather than from the forest or meadow – but their potency remains timeless.

This exquisite album is a portrayal of herbs in all their floral glory. It discovers anecdotes, traditional lore, historical comment and a long-lost era of superstition and magic, together with many herbal remedies.

Herb names have a certain allure … dandelion derives from the French *dents du lion* meaning 'teeth of the lion' after its serrated leaves; dill, often used as a sedative, perhaps comes from the Norse word *dilla* (to lull); the iris has vibrant colours that evoke its namesake, Iris, Greek goddess of the rainbow. The fascinating array of emotions these plants express is also revealed in charts of their meanings (truly 'eating your words'), for many herbs were listed in the Language of Flowers – a secret means to convey emotions to your sweetheart at a time when such matters were generally suppressed: marjoram meant blushes; myrtle signified marriage and love; balsam said, 'touch-me-not'.

The Doctrine of Signatures remained a vital element of folk medicine from the Middle Ages until recent times, drawing upon the notion that if a natural object resembled a certain part of the body it might well cure diseases that arose there – hence the names liverwort, toothwort and lungwort. The importance of herbs was substantial, penetrating multiple facets of daily life, and led to many an Elizabethan and Renaissance knot garden where formal designs enclosed culinary herbs and aromatic plants such as marjoram, thyme, rosemary, lemon balm and mallow. Meanwhile, as the Age of Exploration took European voyagers ever further afield, so many more plants crossed the oceans and were added to the international inventory.

Aside from cuisine, teas, wine, perfume and medicine, herbs have inspired art while some herbs have had spiritual or sacred associations, like basil, aloe, mistletoe and bay. They have also served as a source of dyes, to make cloth, candles, paper and varnish, to ward off evil, to deter mosquitoes, blow bubbles, take you to fairyland and fly broomsticks.

Herbs arouse so many senses – beautiful flowers like the glorious poppy and demure primrose delight the eye and offer tactile pleasures too; there is the texture of silky foxgloves on your fingers

Dandelion

Clover

or a chamomile lawn between your toes; mint, garlic, chives, parsley and all the culinary herbs arouse the taste buds; last but not least, are those scintillating scents. Consider lavender, violets and honeysuckle – exiled French emperor Napoleon Bonaparte claimed that, even across the sea, he could smell his birthplace Corsica with its evocative aromas of myrtle, heather, lavender and thyme.

This mixed array of tasty and aromatic plants has proved a fascinating exploration. Writing such a volume opens doors to the past, to a way of life and changing attitudes through the centuries, even though the herbs themselves have remained a constant throughout the turmoil of history and medical advances. Indeed, the knowledge of past sages (pun intended!) holds many truths today. The order within each section aims to reflect the most commonly used herbs; however, this has proved hard to define, so apologies if anyone feels their particular favourite herb has been 'misranked'.

To avoid repetition and boring verbosity, such phrases as 'It is said…' or 'People once used to believe…' have often been omitted but the omission of precautionary notes in no way implies that the claims are beyond dispute, especially in the case of magic, witches, fairies and miracle cures! I must also apologize that in the space of this little volume we could explore so few of the myriad herbs that begged our attention. The plethora of enticing information proved a challenge to sift, sort, trim and tease into the available pages. But it is a 'taster' – and I hope a very wholesome one – of these truly amazing and very powerful plants.

Lavender; facing page: mixed herbs and garlic.

DISCOVERING THE HERBS

POPULAR CULINARY HERBS

MINT *Mentha*

Aromatic mint has whorls of tiny flowers and serrated leaves – usually dark green but grey-green, golden and purple too. It spreads voraciously underground and is best contained in pots. Mint has ever symbolized hospitality and friendship. Originating in Asia and the Mediterranean, it was used by the Greeks to clean their banqueting tables and in bathwater as a stimulant. The Romans used mint as a digestive aid and mouth freshener and in cordials, fruit compotes and perfumes. Today the USA produces 70 per cent of the world's peppermint and spearmint.

BEST USES AND CULINARY PARTNERS			
FLAVOURS AND TASTES	**COMBINES WITH**	**COMPLEMENTS**	**CULINARY USES**
Aromatic Menthol	Ginger, basil	Lamb, ice cream, salads, fruits, cocktails	Sauces, potatoes, meat, cocktails and candies. Makes an excellent tea, popular in Morocco and other North African nations. Doublemint tea is made from blended peppermint and spearmint

 OVER 30 VARIETIES INCLUDE

American wild mint (*Mentha canadensis*)
Apple and pineapple mint (*Mentha sauveolens*)
Australian mint (*Mentha australis*)
Corsican mint (*Mentha requieinii*)
Garden mint (*Mentha sachalinensis*)
Spearmint and curly mint (*Mentha spicata*)
Peppermint (*Mentha piperita*)
Water or marsh mint (*Mentha aquatic*)

 TRADITIONALLY USED FOR

Stomachache, indigestion, heartburn
Headaches and chest pains
Common colds, breathing and respiratory difficulties
Bad breath
Minor burns
Skin irritations

 DID YOU KNOW?

The name derives from mythical river nymph, Minthe, who caught the eye of Greek Underworld god, Hades. His jealous wife turned Minthe into a plant so that everyone would walk over and crush her but her fine aroma meant that Hades could still sense her presence!
Ancient Hebrews scattered mint over synagogue floors.
Mint has been found in Egyptian tombs dating from 1,000 BC.

 OILS AND REMEDIES

The oil derives from the menthol in its leaves.
It is used in toothpaste, shower gel and medicines.
It is antibacterial.
Cooling, soothing and anti-inflammatory.
Mint contains vitamins A, C and B2.
Mint has minerals like calcium, zinc, copper and magnesium.

PARSLEY *Petroselinum crispum*

Originally from Sardinia, garden parsley spread from there through Italy, Algeria and Tunisia. In the USA the curly variety is the most commonly eaten herb. The flat leaf variety is popular in Continental Europe. The name comes from the Greek *petrose* meaning rock; it grows well on rocky cliffs and beside old stone walls. Ancient Greeks believed parsley sprang from the blood of the hero Archemorus after he was slain by a dragon, and used parsley for ceremonial purposes, as did the Romans who introduced it into every nation they ruled. Parsley is visited by nectar-feeding insects like bees, goldfinches that love the seeds and swallowtail butterflies – whose caterpillars fatten up on it for two busy weeks of munching.

BEST USES AND CULINARY PARTNERS			
FLAVOURS AND TASTES	**COMBINES WITH**	**COMPLEMENTS**	**CULINARY USES**
Savoury Light, fresh, slightly sweet	Basil, bay leaf, dill, chives, garlic, thyme *Bouquet garni* mixes	Garlic butter	Sauces, soups and salads Fish, tomatoes, potatoes and eggs Can make an infusion or tea A most popular herb and garnish

 TRADITIONALLY USED FOR

Gout and rheumatism
Sinus infection and congestion
Bad breath and garlic odours
Excess body water

 DID YOU KNOW?

The Holy Roman Emperor Charlemagne (c.742–814) munched through two cases a year of cheese flavoured with parsley seeds.
Parsley can be hard to establish: whoever can grow it is said to be head of the household – or a witch.
Plucking a sprig while saying one's enemy's name may invoke his or her death.
Corpses were sprinkled with parsley to help reduce the stench.

GARLIC *Allium sativum*

Originating in Asia and known in Ancient Egypt and Africa, garlic (sometimes called the 'stinking rose') is one of the most popular herbs, enjoyed worldwide. Wild, crow and field (or meadow) garlic are joined by wild leek, elephant (pearl or solo) garlic from China, where garlic has been enjoyed since 2,000 BC. Today China is the greatest producer, growing over 77 per cent of the world's output, followed by South Korea, Egypt, Russia and the USA – where garlic flourishes in every state except Alaska; Gilroy in California calls itself the world's 'garlic capital'. Hanging garlic on the front door or in a shop to ward off evil is a widespread tradition, still common practice in India.

BEST USES AND CULINARY PARTNERS			
FLAVOURS AND TASTES	COMBINES WITH	COMPLEMENTS	CULINARY USES
Spicy – mellows and sweetens with cooking	Tomato, onion, ginger, yogurt	Chinese New Year dumplings	Soups and stews, meat, vegetables, breads, oil, pasta, poultry and game

 OILS AND REMEDIES

It is antibiotic and antifungal.
A mosquito repellent; also deters worms, birds and insects.
It prevent colds.
Allixin (a phytoallexin found in garlic) and its analogues
    may be useful in cancer prevention.

 TRADITIONALLY USED FOR

Smallpox, dropsy
Tuberculosis
Parasites
Poor digestion
Respiratory problems
Low energy

? DID YOU KNOW?

Garlic has been used for over 7,000 years.
Garlic 'gods' were invoked by the Egyptians when taking
    oaths.
Garlic is said to ward off vampires, werewolves, witches,
    monsters and demons, especially when worn, hung in
    windows, or rubbed on keyholes and chimneys.
Muslims who have eaten raw garlic are forbidden to pray in
    a mosque.

ROSEMARY *Rosmarinus officinalis*

With its fragrant spiky leaves and lavender-coloured flowers that attract bees, this Mediterranean mint-family member grows in herb gardens as a low hedge or topiary, and thrives in coastal regions. Legends tell how it was draped around the Greek goddess Aphrodite when she rose from the sea and its name means 'dew of the sea'. The Virgin Mary spread her blue cloak over a white rosemary bush when she rested, and the flowers turned sky blue – hence it was dubbed 'Rose of Mary'. It is a remembrance symbol for weddings, war commemorations (sprigs are worn on Australia's ANZAC Day and Remembrance Day), and funerals when mourners sometimes throw it into graves.

BEST USES AND CULINARY PARTNERS			
FLAVOURS AND TASTES	**COMBINES WITH**	**COMPLEMENTS**	**CULINARY USES**
Aromatic and pine-like	Basil, bay, sage, marjoram, oregano, thyme	Barbecued meat, roast potatoes	Flavours stuffings, roast chicken, turkey, lamb, pork and fish Can be sprinkled on bread, soup and lemonade Use rosemary-infused oil on salads or pasta

 ## OILS AND REMEDIES

Rosemary was one of the first essential oils to be distilled, in 1330.
It was burned in sick rooms to kill germs; the scent was thought to be a disinfectant.
Its oil is used in perfumes, incense, shampoo, cleaning products and insect repellents.
The leaves, made into ointments or oil, help cold, numb joints.
It was burned or carried to ward off plague.

 ## TRADITIONALLY USED FOR

Circulatory disorders; gout
Yellow jaundice, coughs, wind
Spots, scars, baldness
Giddiness, loss of speech, headaches
Sore gums; toothache
Bowels and spleen problems
Improving memory and sight
Revitalizing paralyzed limbs

 ## DID YOU KNOW?

Set among barbecue charcoal, it smells like mustard.
Ancient Greeks believed it had magical powers.
In ancient times, students wore sprigs in their hair to improve their memory.
Rosemary was stuffed into cloth dolls to attract a lover or cure an illness.
A sprig under a pillow may stop nightmares.
Rosemary will grow no higher than six feet in 33 years so as not to stand taller than Christ.

 ## FAIRY TALES

In Sicily, it is associated with fairies, who hide under it in the form of snakes.

THYME *Thymus vulgaris*

This low-growing Mediterranean herb has a sweet fragrance and tiny lilac, pink or white flowers with nectar that attracts bees and makes wonderful honey. Green, bronze or silver leaves have multiple aromas but lemon thyme and common thyme are most popular in cuisine. The Romans grew it for bee culture, added it to alcoholic drinks and cheese or used it to treat melancholy. Long-prized as incense for temples and sacrifices, it also signifies courage. Danish and German legends describe it as a fairy favourite, especially near the side of their hills, and an essential ingredient in magic brews that allow you to see the little folk.

BEST USES AND CULINARY PARTNERS			
FLAVOURS AND TASTES	COMBINES WITH	COMPLEMENTS	CULINARY USES
Orange, tangerine, lemon, celery, caraway, pine and eucalyptus	Oregano, rosemary, parsley, sage, savoury	Pork, lamb, duck, or goose	Use leaves and flowers in stuffings, stews, soups, vegetables, casseroles and custards, salads and herbal teas

 ## OILS AND REMEDIES

Thyme essential oil is used in perfumes, soaps, toothpastes and cosmetics.
The oil contains large amounts of thymol, a strong antibacterial agent, antiseptic and antioxidant.
Thymol relieves psoriasis and eczema, septic sore throats, scarlet fever and ringworm.
As a disinfectant, thyme may be twelve times as powerful as carbolic acid.
Baths with thyme relieve joint aches and pains and reduce stress.
The oil can be used in mouthwashes to reduce inflammation and throat infection.
Thyme tea taken three to four times a day will treat coughs.
Fresh thyme with a little syrup may relieve whooping cough.

 ## TRADITIONALLY USED FOR

Asthma and respiratory problems
Bronchitis, upper respiratory tract inflammation
Consumption and whooping cough
Elevating moods and relieving pain
Deodorants

 ## DID YOU KNOW?

Ancient Egyptians used thyme oil in their embalming processes.
There are over 350 thyme species.
It has been recommended as a remedy for nightmares.
It was considered an aphrodisiac and incorporated into love potions.

BASIL *Ocimum basilicum*

First cultivated in India some 5,000 years ago, basil now thrives in Mediterranean areas and Asia. Varieties include sweet, Thai, lemon, Holy and African Blue. Often called the King of Herbs, its name derives from a Greek word for 'king' and the French and Welsh refer to it as a royal herb. Its name is also related to basilisks and scorpions; in African legends, basil protects against scorpions while, in France, smelling basil was thought to breed scorpions in the brain! Jewish folklore suggests it adds strength during a fast and in some religions basil may be placed in the hands or mouth of the dead to secure a safe journey to the next life. Some European legends associate it with Satan.

BEST USES AND CULINARY PARTNERS			
FLAVOURS AND TASTES	**COMBINES WITH**	**COMPLEMENTS**	**CULINARY USES**
Pungent, sweet taste like anise Refreshing bouquet Leaves, flower buds and seeds all edible	Capers, chives, coriander, garlic, marjoram, oregano, mint, onion, parsley, rosemary, thyme, savoury	Tomatoes, salads, pasta, pizza Italian, Greek and Eastern cuisine	Pesto on eggs, meats, cucumber Ice cream, chocolate truffles Beef, chicken, eggs, soups, seafood Artichokes, aubergine, green vegetables Mushrooms, olives, some fruits

 ## OILS AND REMEDIES

Chewing basil leaves or drinking basil tea has a calming effect on the stomach.

Its essential oils have antiviral, antioxidant and antimicrobial effects.

Scientists are investigating using basil oil as an antibiotic and for treating cancer.

It is an element in traditional Indian Ayurveda and Siddha medicine.

 ## TRADITIONALLY USED FOR

Coughs and colds
Headache (especially as a facial steam)
Stings, bites
Ear infections
Regularizing blood-sugar levels
Stress
Relieves indigestion and coughing
Asthma and diabetes (in Indian traditions)

 ## DID YOU KNOW?

Ancient Egyptians and Greeks believed basil would open the gates of heaven.

Basil is revered in Hinduism and the Greek Orthodox Church and is added to holy water.

Basil is associated with the finding of the True Cross by St Helena, mother of Roman Emperor Constantine.

On certain saint days in Portugal, potted basil is traditionally presented to a sweetheart.

In Mexico, a bunch of basil in a shop door or window brings good fortune.

SAGE Garden or common sage *Salvia officinalis*

Latin *salver* means 'to save or heal' and sage was sometimes called 'Sage the Saviour', ever associated with wisdom and longevity and even said to render men immortal. Also called kitchen sage, true sage, culinary sage, and Dalmatian sage, this Mediterranean herb was once considered the most commercially important herb in the USA, but sage was appreciated long before that, as depicted on a Minoan fresco at Knossos, Crete dating to 1,400 BC. Its soft, grey-green leaves and purple flowers attract bees, butterflies, hawk moths and hummingbirds but repel slugs. Old superstitions claim that the plant will thrive or wither according to its owner's fortunes and it was sown on graves to assuage grief.

BEST USES AND CULINARY PARTNERS			
FLAVOURS AND TASTES	**COMBINES WITH**	**COMPLEMENTS**	**CULINARY USES**
Savoury, slightly peppery flavour Warm and pungent	Italian spices Bay leaf, beans, capers, caraway, garlic, ginger, marjoram, onions, paprika, parsley, rosemary, savoury, thyme Vinegar and butter	Pork, poultry, game, seafood	Poultry and pork stuffing Casseroles, sausages, ales, cheese, meat, salads Soups, stews, bread, rice, beans, pork, apples, celery, cheese, citrus, beef, poultry, tomatoes Use leaves in batter or cream, eaten with sugar and orange

 ## TRADITIONALLY USED FOR

Bleeding, wounds, menorrhagia
Warts, ulcers, toothache, sprains,
Swelling, inflammation, rheumatism
Coughs, sore throats, inflamed tonsils
Lung, liver or kidney problems
Headaches, joint pain, rheumatism
Dandruff, perspiration, itching
Assuaging grief and bubonic plague
Cooling fevers and perspiration

 ## OILS AND REMEDIES

Sage is claimed to treat almost every ailment!
It helps to dry up a mother's milk when nursing stops.
Sage strengthens the nervous system, sharpens senses and
improves memory.
Ground sage flowers can be infused to make a light,
soothing herb tea.

 ## DID YOU KNOW?

American Indians used sage as a toothbrush.
The Chinese would trade three chests of Chinese tea for just
one of sage leaves.
Ancient Egyptians used sage as a fertility drug.
Muslims used sage at weddings, in childbirth, and for funeral
rituals.
Sage was burned as incense.
Dried sage leaves among linen discourage insects.

CORIANDER or CILANTRO *Coriandrum sativum*

Coriander grows worldwide, although it was native to temperate Eastern Mediterranean regions and the Middle East. It was enjoyed in ancient Bronze Age and Biblical times – and in Ancient Egypt (coriander mericarps were recovered from Tutankhamen's tomb). Coriander was cultivated in Greece from at least the second millennium BC, with references to its leaves, use in perfume and spicy seeds. A great garnish and flavour enhancer, it was brought to the British-American colonies in 1670 to be grown by early settlers.

BEST USES AND CULINARY PARTNERS			
FLAVOURS AND TASTES	COMBINES WITH	COMPLEMENTS	CULINARY USES
Slightly sweet, citrus-tasting leaves and seeds Grassy, lemony and fresh Coriander roots have a deeper, more intense flavour	Allspice, anise, cardamom, cinnamon, citrus, coriander, curry, fennel, fenugreek, garlic, ginger, grains, mace, onion, nutmeg, orange peel, parsley	Avocados, bay leaf, beans, beef, cabbage, cheese, chicken, coconut, cucumber, fish, fruit, lamb, lentils, peas, pork, potatoes, poultry, rice, sausages, seafood, tomatoes.	Adds a citrus taste to rye bread, pickled vegetables, sausages Use with new potatoes, ham, eggs, pasta, salmon, sauces, green beans, tomatoes, salsa and guacamole Roasted seeds make a snack Beer brewing Thai soups Curry pastes Mediterranean, Caribbean, Mexican, South American, North African, Indian and Southeast Asian cuisines

 ## OILS AND REMEDIES

The leaves are rich in vitamins A, C and K.
Coriander/cilantro has antioxidant properties and can delay food spoilage.
Its diuretic properties and insulin-like activity may control mild diabetes.
Its essential oils serve as an aphrodisiac and cure temporary impotency.

 ## DID YOU KNOW?

Some references to coriander (in India, Egypt, China and Ancient Rome) date back 7,000 years.
Ancient Egyptians believed coriander could be enjoyed in the afterlife.
The name coriander comes from the Greek, *koris*, meaning bed bug.
Coriander is described as an aphrodisiac in *The Arabian Nights* tales.
Sugarplums enjoyed by children (and inspiring the Sugar Plum Fairy in Pyotr Ilyich Tchaikovsky's *The Nutcracker* ballet), were sugar-coated coriander.
People taste coriander leaves differently, depending on their genes.

 ## TRADITIONALLY USED FOR

Improving digestion and appetite
Joint and muscle problems
A laxative and for hemorrhoids
Fungal infections, toothache

CHIVES *Allium schoenoprasum*

From North America, Europe and Asia (the only *Allium* species native to both the Old World and the New), chives are the smallest edible onion and belong to the lily family. Their long slender leaves, scapes and unopened flower buds are all tasty. While their sulfur compounds repel most insects (Japanese farmers planted chives around flowerbeds to deter pests) their pretty pink flowers attract bees. The leaf juice fights mildew, scab and fungal infections. There are also *Allium tuberosum* (called garlic chives, Chinese chives, Oriental garlic, Chinese leeks and kow choi). Romanian gypsies used chives in fortune telling and believed that dried bunches would ward off disease and evil.

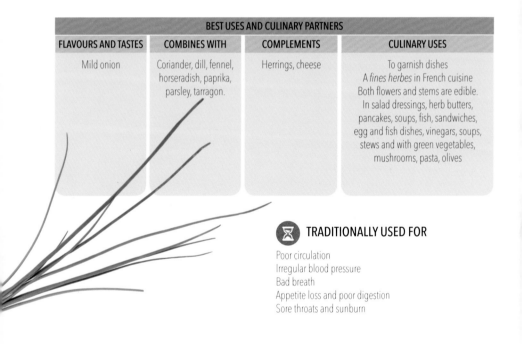

BEST USES AND CULINARY PARTNERS			
FLAVOURS AND TASTES	**COMBINES WITH**	**COMPLEMENTS**	**CULINARY USES**
Mild onion	Coriander, dill, fennel, horseradish, paprika, parsley, tarragon.	Herrings, cheese	To garnish dishes A *fines herbes* in French cuisine Both flowers and stems are edible. In salad dressings, herb butters, pancakes, soups, fish, sandwiches, egg and fish dishes, vinegars, soups, stews and with green vegetables, mushrooms, pasta, olives

 TRADITIONALLY USED FOR

Poor circulation
Irregular blood pressure
Bad breath
Appetite loss and poor digestion
Sore throats and sunburn

 OILS AND REMEDIES

Rich in vitamins A and C.
Contain calcium, iron, potassium and folic acid.
May strengthen nails and teeth.
Has antibiotic properties.
Is a natural insect repellent.
Chives inhibit mildew.

? DID YOU KNOW?

Chives can restore vital nutrients lost in cooking.
Chive recipes from China may be over 5,000 years old.
Dried bunches hung in the house were said to drive away
    disease and evil.
Chives are used in turkey hatchlings' feed.

ROCKET OR ARUGULA *Eruca sativa*

Salad rocket boasts many names including eruca, colewort, garden rocket, rucola and roquette. This popular Mediterranean herb thrives from Morocco and Portugal over to Syria, Lebanon and Turkey and has been enjoyed at least since Roman times when it was noted as an aphrodisiac. A poem ascribed to the Roman author Virgil claimed that 'rocket excites the sexual desire of drowsy people' so monks were forbidden to grow it during the Middle Ages. Later, it had to be set alongside lettuce – said to calm the senses! It has small, cream-white veined flowers with yellow stamens, long seedpods and delicious, deeply-lobed leaves.

BEST USES AND CULINARY PARTNERS			
FLAVOURS AND TASTES	**COMBINES WITH**	**COMPLEMENTS**	**CULINARY USES**
Strong and peppery Nutty and crunchy	Parsley and green salads Seedpods can be a salad item	Sun-dried tomatoes and mozzarella	Salads, soups, potatoes, cheese, seafood, pasta, meats, pizzas Fried in olive oil with garlic for sauces or condiments. Italian straccietti Neapolitan Rucolino liqueur

 OILS AND REMEDIES

Seeds are pressed to make Taramira oil for salad dressings, pickling or cooking in West Asia and India.
Fresh leaves are highly alkaline and rich in antioxidants.
A source of copper, iron, calcium, folic acid, potassium, manganese and phosphorus.
Contains vitamins A, C and K.
Its sulforaphane detoxifies blood and cells and helps promote cancer-preventative enzymes.

 TRADITIONALLY USED FOR

Bone health, gastric ulcers
Alzheimer's disease, diabetes
Anticancer and antimicrobial treatments

 DID YOU KNOW?

A decree by Roman Emperor Charlemagne in 802 declared rocket to be a potherb, suitable for gardens.
Its name reflects its rocket-fast growth speed.
It has been used in English salads since Elizabethan times.
The seed has been an ingredient in aphrodisiacs since the first century AD.

BAY LEAF or LAUREL *Laurus nobilis*

This aromatic evergreen tree is a reminder of the vast laurel forests that once covered much of the Mediterranean area; a few remnants remain in Turkey, Syria, Spain, Portugal, Morocco, the Canary Islands and Madeira. Its green, glossy leaves were an emblem of prosperity and fame and symbolized Christ's resurrection. The Greek sun god, Apollo, wore bay leaves after his beloved Daphne was changed into a bay tree by her father (when Apollo tried to make love to her) and Daphne is the Greek name for the tree. A bay laurel wreath was the prize at the games held in Apollo's honour and became the Roman victory symbol.

BEST USES AND CULINARY PARTNERS			
FLAVOURS AND TASTES	**COMBINES WITH**	**COMPLEMENTS**	**CULINARY USES**
Aromatic bitter-sweet Pungent and sharp Must not be eaten; remove once meal is flavoured Ground bay leaves can be safely ingested Burn on barbecues for a rich scent	Allspice, garlic, grains, juniper, marjoram, oregano, parsley, sage, savoury, thyme	Artichokes, beans, beef, game, lentils, mushrooms, nuts, potatoes, poultry, seafood, tomatoes.	Stocks and soups Italian pasta Bouquet garni Béchamel sauce Fruit compotes and puddings. Bloody Mary cocktails

 OILS AND REMEDIES

Laurel leaves contain essential oils including eucalyptol. The oil is an antibiotic cleanser.
It is anti-fungal and anti-itching.
Its essential oil makes a soothing massage and aromatherapy agent.
An infusion of leaves or berries is a diuretic.
Makes an astringent and salve for open wounds.
Its compounds may inhibit breast- and skin-cancer cell production.

 TRADITIONALLY USED FOR

Stomach aches, painful bruises
Migraines, rheumatism
Stinging nettle, poison ivy and poison oak rashes
Indigestion, earache
Flu, bronchitis, high blood pressure
Bee and wasp stings

 DID YOU KNOW?

The Romans crowned victorious military commanders with bay leaves.
In ancient Greece, poets and scholars wore bay wreaths when they received academic honours.
Poet laureate and baccalaureate derive from laurel's association with achievement.
'Resting on one's laurels' means relying on former glories.
Laurel oil is in Aleppo soap, made for centuries and maybe used by Cleopatra.
In Italy and Turkey shipments of licorice are wrapped in dried bay leaves.
Chinese rice is kept in bay leaves to deter weevils.

DILL or DILL WEED *Anethum graveolens*

The Norse word *dilla* means 'to lull'; Greeks placed dill over their heads to induce sleep but it is also said to be an aphrodisiac. Related to celery, it has clusters of delicate, feathery, aromatic leaves and grows wild among corn in Spain and Portugal. Mentioned in Biblical times, it was a favourite of the Ancient Greeks and Romans and remnants from about 400 BC have been found in Swiss Neolithic settlements. Dill was used in Anglo-Saxon and medieval times for countless ills and was an important herb in witchcraft and spells – once so valuable that it was kept under lock and key.

BEST USES AND CULINARY PARTNERS			
FLAVOURS AND TASTES	**COMBINES WITH**	**COMPLEMENTS**	**CULINARY USES**
Distinctive, pungent and warm Not unlike caraway, but lighter. Hints of anise or lemon	Anise, basil, capers, caraway, chives, fennel, garlic, ginger, horseradish, mint, mustard, oregano, onion, paprika, parsley, tarragon, turmeric	Cucumbers, pickles, tomatoes, salmon, trout, soups like borscht, veal, chicken and turkey breast, hard boiled eggs, omelettes, potatoes, rice, peas and beans, mushrooms, cabbage, carrots, seafood, vinegar	Sprinkle on butter, salads and apple desserts Use with sour cream to make cucumber dressing Can be added to wine Sprinkle on tomatoes Blend into tuna salad Enhance dips

 ## OILS AND REMEDIES

Oil is extracted from leaves, stems and seeds.
Distilled seed oil is used in soap manufacture.
Its essential oils are calming and improve sleep.
Boiling dill in wine and inhaling fumes cures hiccups.
Dill water may soothe babies – and their digestion.
It reduces inflammation, regulates insulin levels, and may prevent certain cancers.

 ## DID YOU KNOW?

Drinks containing dill were thought to destroy evil spells.
The Holy Roman Emperor Charlemagne placed dill on banquet tables to control his guests' flatulence.
In Arab countries, dill seed is called 'grasshopper's eye'.

 ## TRADITIONALLY USED FOR

Indigestion, colic and hiccups
Stimulating intestine
Gas, bloating, stomach pain
Jaundice, bile and liver problems
Headache, arthritis
Boils, ulcers, bad breath
Lack of appetite, nausea
Stimulating milk production
Strengthening nails, bones and brain

MARJORAM Sweet or knotted *Origanum majorana*

Sweet marjoram is sometimes called oregano in the USA and, with that being its Latin name, is often confused with oregano or wild marjoram. It has smooth, aromatic, grey-green leaves and is native to Portugal, Cyprus and Turkey. It was known to the Ancients as a symbol of happiness and planted on graves to bring joy to the dead. Roman couples wore marjoram crowns at their weddings. In medieval and Tudor times it was a strewing herb, a furniture scourer and a perfume. It is still gathered and hung up to dry for making relaxing, sleep-inducing marjoram tea.

BEST USES AND CULINARY PARTNERS			
FLAVOURS AND TASTES	**COMBINES WITH**	**COMPLEMENTS**	**CULINARY USES**
Sweet but with bitter undertones	Basil and thyme; plus cinnamon, cumin, fennel, garlic, onion, oregano, parsley	Artichokes, beans, beef, cheese, eggplant, mushrooms, pizzas, preserved meats, pulses, salads, sausages, seafood, squash, tomatoes, veal	Dressings and sauces, game, poultry, pasta blends, poultry seasonings, soups, and stews, stuffings, tomato dishes, vegetables

 OILS AND REMEDIES

Can be steam-distilled to produce a yellowish essential oil.
Inhaling its infused steam helps clear catarrh.
It is antiseptic, makes a good ointment and is soothing in baths and herbal pillows.
Makes a fine gargle for sore throats.
In heated bags, it eases swellings, rheumatism and colic.
Encourages perspiration and measle-rash eruption.
It is an excellent remedy for the brain.

 TRADITIONALLY USED FOR

Gastric ulcers, indigestion
Spasms, colic, diabetes, dropsy
Headache, toothache, earache
Sprains, bruises, aching stiff muscles
Coughs, colds, sore throats
Narcotic poisons, convulsions

 DID YOU KNOW?

It was grown by medieval monks.
Marjoram dyes wool purple and linen reddish-brown.
It keeps milk sweet and prevents it being turned sour by thunder, hence the name Sweet Marjoram.
Powdered marjoram is in some sneezing powders.

OREGANO OR WILD MARJORAM *Origanum vulgare*

Native to warm temperate Eurasian and Mediterranean zones, oregano has spikes of purple or pink edible flowers and olive-green, spade-like leaves. Its name means 'joy of the mountain'. It became popular in America after US soldiers in 1940s Mediterranean war zones developed a taste for the 'pizza herb'. It is related to marjoram (with which it is often confused) and has long been associated with Italian cuisine although its use probably originated in Greece where it was thought to be precious to the goddess of love, Aphrodite. It is said to have magic powers and, if strewn on the ground, to repel snakes.

BEST USES AND CULINARY PARTNERS			
FLAVOURS AND TASTES	**COMBINES WITH**	**COMPLEMENTS**	**CULINARY USES**
Highly aromatic Ranges from spicy to sweet Many subspecies offer unique flavours Oregano is stronger than marjoram	Basil, garlic, parsley, thyme, olive oil	Bread, lentils, pasta, tomato dishes, eggs, omelettes, cheese dishes and quiche, soups, roast potatoes, beef, kebabs, poultry, veal and stuffings.	Greek, Spanish, Italian, Portuguese, Caribbean and Mexican cuisine

 ## OILS AND REMEDIES

Gently crush dried oregano in your hand to release essential oils.
It has mild antioxidant and antifungal properties.
Dried leaves mixed with honey will fade bruises.
Warm leaf poultices soothe painful swellings.

 ## TRADITIONALLY USED FOR

Sea sickness, calming nerves
Toothache, indigestion
Coughs, headaches

 ## DID YOU KNOW?

Cows grazing where oregano grows may produce tastier meat.
A tortoise who swallows a snake will eat oregano to prevent death!
Anointing yourself with oregano was said to invoke dreams of your future spouse.
It brings good luck and health – and banishes sorrow.

LEMON BALM *Melissa officinalis*

Also known as balm or balm mint, this herb has a sweet, lemon scent and thrives in Southern Europe, North Africa and south-west Asia. Its small, white, nectar-brimming flowers attract many bees and it became a favourite in monastic and cottage gardens. Balm is an abbreviation of balsam, a sweet-smelling oil, while 'melissa' means honey-bee in Greek. It was dedicated to the goddess Diana by the Greeks who used lemon balm some 2,000 years ago. In 1697, *The London Dispensary* recommended that essence of balm, taken in Canary wine, would renew youth, strengthen the brain and prevent baldness. It can also be made into a tea that soothes feverish colds.

BEST USES AND CULINARY PARTNERS			
FLAVOURS AND TASTES	COMBINES WITH	COMPLEMENTS	CULINARY USES
A sweet citrus flavour Aromatic leaves	Peppermint, nettle and chamomile	Fish, poultry, sauces, pesto, salads, fruit salads, mushrooms, cheese dishes	Use in jam, jellies, candies and ice cream Flavours vermouth and cordials called *Tea de France*

 ## TRADITIONALLY USED FOR

Melancholy, vomiting, vertigo
Mad-dog bites, scorpion stings
Gastrointestinal tract, nervous system, liver
Menstrual tension and cramping
Allergies, stress, anxiety, depression
Flatulence, indigestion, heart palpitations
Overindulgence in mushrooms
Cleansing sores and wounds
Improving memory; sharpening brain and wit
Promoting perspiration to relieve fever
Easing spasms, tension, colic, gout
Repelling insects (including mosquitoes)
Healing wounds

 ## OILS AND REMEDIES

Lemon balm oil is used in perfumery.
It will relax and soothe aromatherapy patients.
It is antiviral, antibacterial and anti-histaminic.
A mild soothing sedative, it relieves insomnia.
It makes surgical dressings antiputrescent.
Its volatile oils include citral, citronella and eugenol.

 ## DID YOU KNOW?

Balm improves honey production.
People used to rub beehives with balm leaves to encourage bees to keep together.
For 50 years, John Hussey breakfasted on balm tea with honey; he lived to 116.
Lemon balm grew in monasteries' apothecary gardens; it was used for dressing wounds and to make perfumes and liquors.

FENNEL *Foeniculum vulgare*

Fennel's Latin name derives from *foenum* (fragrant hay), while the Greeks dubbed it *marathon* after the famous battle in 490 BC which erupted on a field of fennel. With feathery leaves, succulent shoots and aromatic fruit, fennel thrives in much of temperate Europe, especially Mediterranean shores, from whence it spread to India and Persia. The florence fennel, also called finocchio, gives swollen bulbs that are eaten as vegetables. In ancient times a symbol of success, it was said to greatly improve strength and eyesight. The Roman historian and writer Pliny observed that serpents ate it when casting their old skins and sharpened their sight by rubbing against it. Fennel was draped over doors on Midsummer's Eve to ward off evil.

BEST USES AND CULINARY PARTNERS			
FLAVOURS AND TASTES	**COMBINES WITH**	**COMPLEMENTS**	**CULINARY USES**
Like anise or licorice	Peppers and curry	Soups, salmon and mackerel	Raw in salads As a vegetable In sausages, bread, pickles, tomato sauce, Italian *Cartucci*, liqueurs To flavour mead drinks

 ## OILS AND REMEDIES

The oil is used in sugars, candy, cordials, liqueur, soap-scenting and perfume.
The seeds make a gripe water for colicky babies.
Its stalks may induce sleep.
Leaves, seeds and roots boiled in barley water make a slimming aid.

 ## TRADITIONALLY USED FOR

Wind, hiccups, nausea
Yellow jaundice, gout, cramp
Shortness of breath, wheezing, bronchial spasms
Stomach muscle or intestinal problems
Bad breath
Serpent bites, mushroom poisoning

 ## DID YOU KNOW?

Powdered fennel deters fleas in kennels and stables.
A medieval German monk was cured of an eye cataract with a fennel root decoction.
Fennel seeds were chewed by Puritans during long services to stop hunger pangs and tummy rumbles.
It reduces flatulence in dogs.

TARRAGON *Artemisia dracunculus*

Tarragon, with its glossy green leaves and clusters of greenish-yellow florets, has Russian and Central Asian origins and, despite being known to the Greeks in 500 BC, was slow to spread. By the 1400s it had been brought by the Arabs to Spain and thence reached France – where it has been influential in cuisine ever since. French tarragon cannot easily be grown from seed, only by root division, and likes a hot, sunny spot. The name has Persian and Arabic roots: *turkhum* means dragon and was possibly inspired by the herb's fiery taste or its serpentine roots.

BEST USES AND CULINARY PARTNERS			
FLAVOURS AND TASTES	COMBINES WITH	COMPLEMENTS	CULINARY USES
Distinctive, sweet, anise flavour Spicy, sharp, aromatic Russian tarragon is slightly bitter and spikes the appetite	Basil, bay leaf, capers, chives, citrus, dill, garlic, onion, oregano, parsley, thyme Used cautiously, it enhances other herbs	Egg dishes, soups (especially chicken) stews, cheeses, poultry, fish, vinegar, pickles, relishes, fish, veal, tomato and egg dishes, artichokes, carrots, green vegetables, mushrooms, potatoes, seafood	Mayonnaise, mustards, Bearnaise sauce, tarragon vinegar, sauce tartare and French *fines herbes* Pickles, fresh green salads, white sauces, butters and purées Tarhun, a popular soft drink in Eastern Europe Slovenia's potica, a sweet, nut-roll cake Young stems make an asparagus substitute

 OILS AND REMEDIES

Fresh tarragon's essential volatile oil is chemically identical with anise's.
It breaks down fats and proteins, helping digestion.
Young leaves are rich in iodine, mineral salts, vitamins A and C.
Calming tarragon tea soothes insomnia.

 TRADITIONALLY USED FOR

Toothache, scurvy
Rheumatoid and arthritic pain
Mad-dog bites, venomous stings
Sedatives and digestive tonics
Calming hyperactivity

 DID YOU KNOW?

Tarragon is called Little Dragon, Mugwort or (in French) *estragon*, Dragon's Herb.
The serpentine shape of its root led ancient herbalists to believe that it could cure snake bites.
A drink of mixed tarragon and fennel juice was enjoyed by Indian royalty.
The green leaves are best picked between Midsummer and Michaelmas.

FLORAL HEALING HERBS

PRIMULA OR PRIMROSE *Primula vulgaris*

Primulas grow wild in the northern hemisphere and have spread south into tropical mountains as far removed as Ethiopia, Indonesia, New Guinea and South America. Almost half of the known species are from the Himalayas. The name comes from primus, meaning first or early: the sweet, gentle flowers of *Primula vulgaris* open in early spring on banks and verges, attracting butterflies by day and moths by night. Its five petals represent birth, initiation, consummation, repose and death; six-petals bring luck in love and marriage. Volcanologists claim that primroses open up their petals just before a volcanic eruption.

BEST USES AND CULINARY PARTNERS	
COMPLEMENTS	CULINARY USES
Salads	Young leaves and fresh flowers are tasty raw Boiled softened leaves can be eaten Relishes are made from the roots Their crystallised flowers make cake decorations Flowers can be made into jam and wine Dried primrose can be used to make teas

 TRADITIONALLY USED FOR

Restlessness and insomnia
Fits, paralysis, rheumatism
Worms in animals
Spots – rub stem juice onto the face
Making love potions
Planting on children's graves

 OILS AND REMEDIES

Primrose leaves make a fine salve to heal wounds.
The Greeks believed primroses had great healing power, overcoming disease and paralysis.
Hampshire woodmen boiled primroses in lard to make an ointment.

 DID YOU KNOW?

Primroses originated in Paradise! One day Saint Paul fell asleep at the Pearly Gates and dropped the keys to Heaven. An angel fetched them back from Earth but where once the golden keys had lain, the first primroses emerged.
The first girl to find a primrose at Easter would marry that year.
Primrose Day (19 April) marks the anniversary of the death of British prime minister Benjamin Disraeli (1804–81); it was his favourite flower.
Less than a handful of primroses indoors endangers one's ducklings!
A single primrose leads to hens laying bad eggs; dance around it three times to keep hens safe.

FAIRY TALES

Touching a fairy rock with the right number of primroses leads you to Fairyland.
Eating primroses or peering over the petals would give children a glimpse of the little folk.
Posies left on doorsteps meant that fairies would bless the house and its occupants – or be kept out!!

FIELD POPPY *Papaver rhoeas*

Poppy seed can lie dormant for over 80 years but during the First World War an estimated 2,500 poppy seeds per square foot were brought to the surface by the turmoil and germinated; sheets of red blooms spread across the battlefields. The Ancient Greeks associated poppies with fertility and many civilizations believed they would have bountiful crops if poppies grew in their fields, hence the name 'corn poppy'. Cultivated since 5,000 BC in Mesopotamia and found in Egyptian tombs, other common names include Flanders poppy, corn rose and redweed.

BEST USES AND CULINARY PARTNERS	
COMPLEMENTS	**CULINARY USES**
Seeds complement bread, cakes and vegetables	Petals make a syrup for soups and gruels

 ## OILS AND REMEDIES

Poppy oil is a substitute for olive oil.
Ancient Greek doctor Hippocrates (460–377 BC) described poppy juice as narcotic, hypnotic and cathartic.
Poppy syrup would procure rest and sleep for the sick and weak. The witch in L. Frank Baum's *The Wonderful Wizard of Oz* said: 'Poppies. Poppies will put them to sleep.'
Early Greeks may have used poppy extracts as a form of euthanasia.
Morphine and codeine alkaloids, found in poppies, are vital drugs.
Black poppy seeds boiled in wine ease menstruation pain.

 ## TRADITIONALLY USED FOR

Catarrhs, coughs, consumption
Sore throats, voice loss
Head pains, toothache
St Anthony's fire
Inflammation, ague, gout
Falling sickness, pleurisy
Insomnia and pain relief

 ## DID YOU KNOW?

A poppy goddess was worshipped in Minoan Crete.
Poppy odour may cause headaches; the flowers were sometimes called 'headache' or 'headwork'.
Syrup from the petals was used to colour ink.
The California poppy has been California's state flower since 1903.
In Persian literature red corn poppies are the flower of love.

OPIUM POPPY *Papaver somniferum*

Images of opium poppies appear in Sumeria about 4,000 BC. The ancient Minoans certainly made opium so its effects were known millennia ago. Its Latin name means 'sleep-bringing poppy', referring to its use as a sedative and narcotic. Morphine, codeine and heroin are derived from both the fresh plant and its mown straw. The seeds have long been used to aid sleeping, fertility and wealth and, so folk tales tell, for magical invisibility. Sadly, this beautiful ornamental plant has also introduced society to drug addiction and so is illegal for recreational use.

BEST USES AND CULINARY PARTNERS	
COMPLEMENTS	**CULINARY USES**
Soups and stews Breads	The foliage serves as a vegetable The petal syrup is an ingredient in soups and gruels Poppy seeds can be used whole or ground

 ## OILS AND REMEDIES

Patent medicines made with opium included Batley's Sedative Solution, Dalby's Carminative, Godfrey's Cordial, McMunn's Elixir, and Mother Bailey's Quieting Syrup.

Opium flowers and seedheads appear on the Royal College of Anaesthetists' coat of arms.

The pressed seeds yield a healthy oil.

Leaves and seedheads were boiled in water to make juice, or pressed and rubbed to create tablets.

In the 1800s, morphine was used in surgery as an anaesthetic.

American Civil War soldiers injected themselves with morphine before removing bullets.

 ## TRADITIONALLY USED FOR

Stomach problems, indigestion
Bad eyesight, insomnia, asthma
Childbirth, pain relief

 ## DID YOU KNOW?

The Opium Wars in 1839–42 and 1856–60 broke out when the Chinese tried to stop Western traders smuggling opium into their country; 25 per cent of Chinese men were addicted, smoking it in opium dens.

On the television show Mythbusters, subjects tested positive for narcotics after eating just four poppy seed bagels!

Many nineteenth-century Romantic writers were inspired under the influence of opium – including Lord Byron, George Crabbe, John Keats, Thomas de Quincy (*Confessions of an English Opium Eater*) and Percy Shelley – as was French Romantic composer Hector Berlioz.

The poem *Kublai Khan* was conceived by Samuel Taylor Coleridge while taking opium to counteract dysentery.

 **WARNING** Opium is a narcotic.

FOXGLOVE *Digitalis purpurea*

Foxgloves relish woodland clearings, hedges, moorland, sea-cliffs and mountain slopes in Europe, Africa, Asia and Australasia. The name was inspired by their fingered glove shape (supposedly worn by foxes) and the Old English *'folk's* glove' – after the fairies who hid inside and made the bell-like blooms ring. Spots inside blossoms marked where elves had touched them! These tall, stately, mauve-pink or white spires are also called fingerhut, fairy thimbles, fairy caps, fairy petticoats, witches' thimbles or Virgin Mary's Glove. Legends tell how foxes begged for protection against hunters so God put bell-shaped flowers in the field to ring out a warning if any were nearby.

 OILS AND REMEDIES

Today digitalis is an invaluable cardiac drug, used as a stimulant in heart medicine and atrial fibrillation and to reduce eye pressure in glaucoma patients.
Foxglove leaves were used to darken lines and patterns engraved on stone floors.

 TRADITIONALLY USED FOR

Poisonous plant: do not try these at home
Sprains and bruises
Dropsy, falling sickness
Scabby heads and old sores
Internal haemorrhage
Epilepsy, acute mania

 DID YOU KNOW?

Witches grew foxgloves in their gardens as an ingredient for spells.
Foxgloves keep evil at bay in the garden but are unlucky indoors.
Foxes wear them as gloves and boots to be quiet if hunting or raiding hencoops.

 FAIRY TALES

Picking a foxglove offends the fairies but if they steal your baby, then foxglove juice may help you win it back.
Fairies inside the plants make a magic thunder sound when children strike the flower's bell.

 POISONS AND TOXINS

The entire plant (roots and seeds and all) is extremely toxic, causing nausea, vomiting, diarrhoea, stomach pain, delirium, wild hallucinations and severe headache.
Foxgloves stimulate the kidneys to release excess fluid and were a recommended purge for the liver and spleen.
From ancient times, herbalists have used digitalis in controlled circumstances for medicinal purposes.
Dutch painter Vincent Van Gogh's Yellow Period may have been partly due to his digitalis therapy, to control seizures.

 WARNING The entire plant is toxic.

HONEYSUCKLE OR WOODBINE *Lonicera*

Of some 180 species of honeysuckle, 100 occur in China but honeysuckle also thrives in Europe, India and North America where its delicious, fruity scent attracts hummingbirds and butterflies. It has exquisite, creamy yellow or rosy, whorled trumpets and strong fibrous stems that can serve as textiles and for binding. Honeysuckle was often grown around doors to ward off witches and evil spirits. If placed under a pillow, it was believed to invoke pleasant dreams and happy moods and is still used in aromatherapy pillows.

BEST USES AND CULINARY PARTNERS
CULINARY USES

The fruit is generally toxic
Sucking the sweet flowers has long been a childhood pursuit
A hot tea can be made from the flowers

 ## OILS AND REMEDIES

Honeysuckle oil warms the body.
A syrup made from the flowers eases coughs and asthma.
It has a broad-spectrum, antiviral impact.
One recently isolated molecule targets influenza viruses,
   including Spanish and avian flu.
A honeysuckle poultice reduces skin rashes and poison-oak
   effects.
As an external infusion, it reduces infection risks in cuts.
Together with chrysanthemum, it lowers blood pressure and
   is a diuretic and kidney stimulant.
Used in herbal medicine since 659 AD to inhibit germs.
One of the 50 fundamental herbs in Chinese herbology.
Anti-inflammatory, antibacterial, calming.

 ## TRADITIONALLY USED FOR

Fevers, common colds
Skin infections, rashes, freckles, sunburn
Rheumatism and arthritis
Ulcers, sore throats
Clearing lungs and asthma
Dysentery and diarrhoea
Speeding up childbirth
Cramps and convulsions
An expectorant
Clearing away toxic substances

 ## DID YOU KNOW?

Bears and birds enjoy eating the berries and suffer no ill
   effects.
Cat toys may be stuffed with honeysuckle as felines like the
   scent.
Lonicera is named after Renaissance botanist, Adam Lonicer.
Dye is made from the berries.

 **WARNING** The fruit is toxic.

MEADOW CRANESBILL *Geranium pretense* and *Geranium maculatum*

Along with wild cranesbill and storksbill, this delicate, five-petalled flower is usually purple to blue but may also be pink or white – often with distinct veining. Named after its pointed seedpods that resemble a long crane's bill, it flourishes on chalk soils, grasslands, damp woodland, thickets, hedges and roadside verges, and in meadows – and gardens. Its many varieties grow from 23 centimetres (9 inches) to over 1.2 metres (4 feet) tall, flowering abundantly in midsummer.

BEST USES AND CULINARY PARTNERS	
COMPLEMENTS	CULINARY USES
Jellies, cakes, and vinegars	Leaves can be used to make tea

 OILS AND REMEDIES

Geranium essential oil helps to make rose-scented oil in perfumes.

Add pre-soaked leaves to bath water to soothe rheumatism.

The blackfeet tribe of Native Americans used sticky geranium to treat diarrhoea, gastric problems and urinary irritations.

Roots were used by Native Americans to stop external bleeding.

Bloody cranesbill arrests bleeding and helps heal wounds.

A natural treatment for diabetic vision problems.

The brown tail and mouse moth enjoy eating cranesbill.

 TRADITIONALLY USED FOR

Diarrhoea, dysentery

Summer complaint (cholera infantum)

Blood disorders, hemorrhages

Excessive menstruation

Uterine and internal bleeding

Ulcers (and a throat gargle to kill germs)

Bladder inflammation, Chron's disease

Hemorrhoids

Eye conjunctivitis and retina irritation

Blood pressure, small doses of cranesbill raise this; larger doses lower it

 DID YOU KNOW?

The cranesbill arrived in Finland during the First World War among German soldiers' provisions!

In autumn, bloody cranesbill leaves turn crimson

Bloody cranesbill roots make a red dye.

NASTURTIUM *Tropaeolum*

Fiery jungle plants, nasturtiums have brilliant, showy, yellow, orange or red flowers, with five petals and a funnel-shaped spur. *Tropaeolum* is the flowering species; *Nasturtium officiale* is the watercress variety. The first *Tropaeolum* were imported from South America into Spain in 1569 and reached England in 1597. It was named by Swedish botanist Carl Linnaeus to reflect the Roman post-battle, victory custom of setting up a trophy pole called a *tropaeum* decorated with the weapons and armour of vanquished foes; nasturtiums' round leaves do resemble shields and the flowers, blood-stained helmets.

BEST USES AND CULINARY PARTNERS	
COMPLEMENTS	CULINARY USES
Salad, butter, cream cheese, cucumber, potato salad	The peppery leaves and flowers have a tangy flavour Pickled unripe flower buds and seedpods serve as capers Some tubers are a popular treat in the Andes Leaves and petals seeped in hot water make a tea Use in stir fries, omelettes, fritters, spiced vinegar and soups

 OILS AND REMEDIES

Facial masks and washes can be made with the leaves.
It promotes the formation of new blood cells.
T. majus treats respiratory and urinary tract infections.
Ground leaves or petals make an antibiotic, antiseptic and antifungal ointment.
The tea alleviates respiratory infections and stimulates the digestive tract.

 TRADITIONALLY USED FOR

Bronchitis and chest colds
Cuts and scrapes
Acne, skin irritations, scurvy
Stimulating hair growth
An insecticide
An antiseptic and expectorant
A fine source of vitamin C and iron

 DID YOU KNOW?

The name nasturtium comes Latin *nasus tortus*, meaning 'twisted nose' – perhaps the effect it has on us when we smell it!
Many shampoos and conditioners include nasturtium.
In World War Two, nasturtium seeds were a pepper substitute.
Hardy *T. polyphyllum* survives 3,300 metres (10,000 feet) high in the Chilean Andes.

IRIS AND ITS ROOT ORRIS *Iris*

This elegant flower grows in rocky areas, meadows, lake and riversides, exhuberant in its rainbow colours. Iris (Greek goddess of lost love and grief) carried messages from heaven to Earth, using the rainbows as her pathway. She led young girls into the afterlife and Greek men often planted an iris on their beloved's grave. Early depictions include a fresco in King Minos's palace in Crete dating to about 2,100 BC. Ancient Egyptians placed an iris on royal sceptres and the Sphinx's brow – its three petals signifying faith, wisdom and valour. Clothworkers and launderers used the root to make clothes and linen smell sweet.

BEST USES AND CULINARY PARTNERS	
COMPLEMENTS	CULINARY USES
Gin and brandy Russian honey and ginger drinks	Raspberry-like flavouring

 ## OILS AND REMEDIES

Orris is an essential oil derived from the roots of *Iris germanica* and *Iris pallida*.
In ancient Greece and Rome, it was used in perfume and unguents to soften skin.
Orris strengthens fragrances in powders, perfume, toothpastes and potpourri.
One ton of iris root produces two kilos of essential oil.
Physic writers stated it was a strong purge.
Taken in small doses with red wine, it regularized heavy menses.
Native Americans used it to ease earache and as a paste to treat wounds and ulcers.

 ## DID YOU KNOW?

Irises were painted by Leonardo da Vinci, Durer, Renoir, Cezanne, Gauguin, Monet and Vincent Van Gogh (whose *Irises* sold for over 53 million dollars).
England's King Edward III put the iris on his royal coat of arms.
It is a state flower of Tennessee, celebrated in an annual festival.
A stylized iris appears in the French royal fleur-de-lis, as the scouting symbol, on the Quebec flag and Florence's and Brussels' coat of arms.
Orris root can be used to make ornamental beads or infant teething rings.
Queen Elizabeth I of England wore a gown embroidered with irises.

 ## TRADITIONALLY USED FOR

Liver, pancreas, kidneys and goiter
Gastric pain, diarrhoea, jaundice
Stomach discharges, migraine,
Psoriasis, eczema, open ulcers
Skin infections, syphilis, dropsy
Nausea, vomiting, morning sickness
Bad breath; as a snuff to provoke sneezing
Reducing freckles

LAVENDER *Lavandula officinalis* and *Lavandula angustifolia*

Its name deriving from the Latin *lavare* (to wash) or *livere* (blueish), lavender hails from the Pyrenees, western Mediterranean, Cape Verde and the Canaries. With its spikes of blue or lilac whorls, today it flourishes in parts of Africa and Asia, including India. English Lavender is far more aromatic than the French, and the delicate-scented oil fetches ten times the price. Lavender was used in Ancient Egypt for cosmetics and embalming; Tutankhamen's tomb revealed jars filled with ungents possibly containing lavender. Since the 1500s lavender has scented knot gardens and lined paths.

BEST USES AND CULINARY PARTNERS	
COMPLEMENTS	**CULINARY USES**
Syrup, cheeses, salads, cakes, desserts	Lavender's rich nectar produces delicious honey Its candied flowers make sweet cake decorations Herbal teas, chocolate, scones, marshmallows

 ## OILS AND REMEDIES

The buds contain oil used in massage therapy, balms, salves, perfumes, cosmetics and bath oils.
Its essential oil is antiseptic and anti-inflammatory.
The oil was used in World War I hospitals.
Both petals and oil are used in soap and pillows.
A 2013 survey stated that lavender oil may be effective in the treatment of neurolgical disorders.
It can perfume linen, clothing, gloves and leather.
Dried lavender is great for potpourris and wedding confetti.
The oil was used to embalm corpses.
Lavender honey is good for wounds.
Its infusions help relaxation and sleep.

 ## TRADITIONALLY USED FOR

Acne, bruises, insect bites
Anxiety, faintness, giddiness, spasms
Burns, inflamed skin, wounds
Rheumatism, sprains, stiff joints
Hysteria, palsy, tension, exhaustion
Flatulence, colic, insomnia
Headaches, toothache, neuralgia
Sinuses, headaches, hangovers
Hoarseness, voice loss.
Soothing the feet

 ## DID YOU KNOW?

People once thought vipers lived in lavender.
It was one of the holy herbs used in Solomon's temple.
Bunches of lavender repel insects, including moths, and kill parasites like lice.
French lavender was an ingredient in Four Thieves' Vinegar, popular in the Middle Ages to protect against plague and used by graverobbers to wash plague victims' belongings.
The Pilgrim Fathers took lavender with them to America.

SWEET VIOLET *Viola odorata*

Harbingers of spring, purple, lilac or white petals glow amid heart-shaped leaves in shady woodland clearings and banks. These delicate flowers are surprisingly virile, with deep roots and spreading runners. Names include Hearts Ease, Bird's Eye, Love Idol, Three-faces-under-a-hood and Jack-jump-up-and-kiss-me. *Viola* is the Latin form of Greek *Ione* – from Io, whom the god Zeus or Jupiter adored but was forced to turn into a white heifer; he then gave her violets to eat. Its chemical constituents (named, after her, ionones) desensitize nose receptors so the sweet scent is fleeting. Powerful against 'wykked sperytis', violets have long been associated with youthful death.

BEST USES AND CULINARY PARTNERS	
COMPLEMENTS	**CULINARY USES**
Syrup of Violets flavours soufflés, cream, desserts, liqueurs, scones and marshmallows Fresh flowers work in chocolates, salads, stuffings and raspberries	Violet flower wine (popular with the Romans) To lend vinegar a beautiful colour A main ingredient of sherbet Candied flowers decorate desserts

 OILS AND REMEDIES

Violet root and vinegar treat gout and spleen problems.
Violet head-garlands dispel wine fumes, preventing headache and dizziness.
The syrup eases inflammation and sore throats, soothes headaches and helps sleep.
A poultice of green leaves, fried with egg yolk, soothes the heat of piles.
Violet leaves allay the pain of cancerous growths, especially in the throat.
Violet perfume, made in Grasse (France), has been popular since the 1800s.

 TRADITIONALLY USED FOR

Anger, insomnia, constipation
Urinary complaints and gravel
Ague, epilepsy, pleurisy
Jaundice, quinsy, falling sickness
Eye inflammation
Swellings, bruises, rheumatism
Consumption, lung diseases, coughs
Plasters, poultices, emetics

? DID YOU KNOW?

Violets were the official symbol of Ancient Athens.
Napoleon made the violet his signature flower and covered Josephine's grave with them.
Country folk would not allow violets indoors, fearing they carried fleas.
Many of its 200 or so names relate to love and sex.
Violet leaves contain vitamin A and are very high in vitamin C.
The term 'shrinking violet' means a shy girl.
The Celts said that, steeped in goats' milk, violets improve feminine beauty.
Like litmus, their flower infusion distinguishes acids from alkalis.

MORNING GLORY *Ipomoea*

Morning glory is just one of the convolvulus family which boasts over 500 species, including morning glory, bindweed and moonflower – all twist and scramble prolifically (Latin *convolvo* means to twine around). They produce funnel-like trumpets in white, blue and pink, with gorgeous striped varieties, too. *Ipomoea* heralds from tropical and subtropical regions; bindweed from more temperate zones. Moonflowers are night-blooming, often heavily fragrant. Because its blooms are so short-lived (literally one morning's glory!) the flower stands for 'farewell' in the Language of Flowers. Certain species were used by the Aztecs and Zaoptecs to give their victims weird hallucinations, not to mention extreme nausea and diarrhoea.

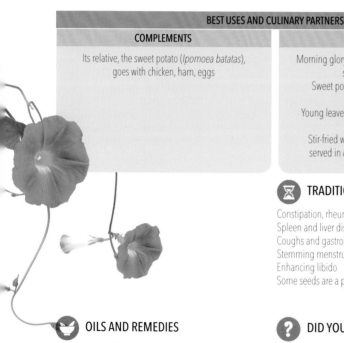

BEST USES AND CULINARY PARTNERS	
COMPLEMENTS	**CULINARY USES**
Its relative, the sweet potato (*Ipomoea batatas*), goes with chicken, ham, eggs	Morning glory is not normally eaten although some seeds can give you a 'trip' Sweet potato is a starchy, sweet-tasting root vegetable Young leaves and shoots are sometimes eaten as greens Stir-fried water spinach (*Ipomoea aquatica*) is served in Asia and warmer American regions

⌛ TRADITIONALLY USED FOR

Constipation, rheumatism
Spleen and liver diseases or enlargement
Coughs and gastrointestinal disorders
Stemming menstrual bleeding
Enhancing libido
Some seeds are a psychedelic drug

OILS AND REMEDIES

Ipomoea purge: The drug Jalap, from its root resin, relieves constipation and bowel colic.
Ipomea hederacea: (ivy-leaf): Seeds are diuretic, laxative, anti-inflammatory, act as a blood purifier and soothe abdominal diseases, fevers, headache, bronchitis.
Ipomoea digitata (alligator yam): A tonic in India and Southeast Asia; prevents obesity, regularizes menstruation.

? DID YOU KNOW?

Convolvulus rhodorhiza produces rodium oil, used by ratcatchers to lure rodents.
Field bindweed (*Convolvulus arvensis*) takes only an hour and three-quarters to make a complete twist around another flower's stem.
The dried tubers of *Ipomoea jalapa* (John the Conqueror) look like testicles and are rubbed for good luck in sexual conquests.
In about 1,600 BC, Mesoamerican Olmecs used the moonvine as part of the rubber-making process when making balls for their games.

COWSLIP *Primula Veris*

Also called fairy cups (fairies hid in them!), cowslips enjoy open meadows, coastal dunes and cliffs in temperate Europe and Asia, especially Pakistan. Once endangered in the UK, they are now protected and flourish. The name may derive from Old English *couslyppe* – meaning cow dung (where they often grow) – or from their boggy habitat. An ingredient of druids' magical potions and a good luck symbol, in Norse mythology they were dedicated to the goddess Freya, and were the key to her treasure trove, an attribute later transferred to the Virgin Mary. By the Middle Ages the cowslip was called St Peter's Herb and was part of the apothecary's 'toolkit'.

BEST USES AND CULINARY PARTNERS	
COMPLEMENTS	**CULINARY USES**
Salads, wine and vinegars	To stuff meat Crystallized for desserts Made into preserves and jam

 ## OILS AND REMEDIES

Cowslip wine is a sedative, inducing sleep.
It may be slightly narcotic.
Ancient Greeks believed cowslips could cure paralysis and palsy.
The powdered root, boiled in ale, cured hysterics.
Cowslips, infused in white wine, improve the complexion, drive away wrinkles and remove freckles.
The flower juice deters spots, pimples and wrinkles.

 ## DID YOU KNOW?

Nightingales like their fragrance and fly where cowslips grow.
Scatter cowslip flowers on your threshold to deter visitors.
Wash your face in cowslip-infused milk to attract the man of your dreams.
Cowslips planted on Good Friday turn into primroses.
Folk names include peggle, key of heaven, buckles, palsywort, plumrocks and tittypines.

 ## FAIRY TALES

Cowslips help you to find fairy gold and secret treasure.

TRADITIONALLY USED FOR

Insomnia, coughs
Rheumatism and gout
Wounds, sunburn
Headaches and migraine
Nerves, anxiety, restlessness
Vertigo, convulsions, trembling
Falling sickness, amnesia
Cramps, back and bladder pain
Winter depression, kidney problems
Strengthening the brain
Palsy strokes and hallucinations

ORCHID *Orchidaceae*

The vast orchid family has 21,000 to 26,000 species, 880 genera and comprises six to eleven per cent of all seeding plants. The name (from Ancient Greek *órkhis*) means testicle – after the twin tubers some sport. All are exquisitely delicate. In cooler climes, they are secretive and restrained; carmine, purple and pale lilac spikes appear fleetingly in damp meadows. Exotic tropical orchids are the world's most spectacular flowers. Many self-pollinate. Some, like the fly, butterfly or bee orchid, mimic insects; real insects may attempt to mate with and thus fertilize the flowers. Their beauty caused 'orchid fever' in the 1800s: avid collectors rushed to the jungle, where many died, lost or succumbing to tropical diseases.

BEST USES AND CULINARY PARTNERS	
COMPLEMENTS	**CULINARY USES**
Salads and stir-fries Orchid tubers flavour meat sauces	All orchids are edible The vanilla vine species in Central and South America and Madagascar; sweet vanilla beans have been collected for centuries and have been a horticultural crop for about 150 years Flowers can be candied for cake decorations Middle Eastern and Turkish cooks use the tubers in ice cream The rich fibrous root helps digestion

 TRADITIONALLY USED FOR

Boosting immune system
Cancer treatment
Improving eyesight
Regaining strength after illness

 OILS AND REMEDIES

The Chinese described using orchids in medicine 3,000 years ago.
Dendrobium officinale has been a medical ingredient for centuries.
Powdered Chinese Ground Orchid (*Bletilla striata*) stops excessive bleeding.
At least 50 orchid species serve traditional medicine.
Stems and bulbs are highly nutritious.

 DID YOU KNOW?

The UK's rare Lady's Slipper and Dark Red Helleborine orchids are permanently guarded.
Ghost orchids can vanish for a long time – resurfacing after perhaps twenty years.
There are four times more orchid species than mammals, twice as many as bird species and about the same as bony fish.
First Lady orchids were launched in 1929, named for the wife of US president Herbert Hoover.
Orchids offer a full range of tastes from sweet to bitter, and have a mix of endive and cucumber flavours.

OX-EYE DAISY *Leucanthemum vulgare*

This bright daisy, with some twenty gleaming, white florets centred on its golden yellow hub, flourishes in fields, grassy banks, roadside verges, railway embankments and open woodlands in Europe and temperate Asia – attracting bees, butterflies and hoverflies. It is called midsummer daisy, love-me-not, Herb Margaret, dog- moon- and Dun daisy (after the thunder god), and Maudlin Daisy or Maudlinwort (after Mary Magdalen). Invasive, it spreads from rhizome fragments and a zillion seeds that remain viable for six years or so.

BEST USES AND CULINARY PARTNERS	
COMPLEMENTS	CULINARY USES
Add flowers to salads or desserts	The edible root can be eaten raw or cooked Marinated, the unopened flower buds provide an alternative to capers The flower can be tempura-battered, similar to pineapple Offers an aromatic, bitter, tingling taste

 OILS AND REMEDIES

In early summer daisies should be collected, dried and stored.

This herb works as oils, ointments, plasters and syrups for treating wounds..

Apply bruised leaves to reduce swellings.

Its tea will relax the bronchials.

During the Middle Ages, ox-eye daisies were used to treat madness, tumours and smallpox.

 TRADITIONALLY USED FOR

Asthma, whooping-cough
Nervous excitability, nightsweats
Yellow jaundice, stomach ulcers
Palsy, sciatica or gout
Colic and digestive upsets
Lotions for wounds, bruises, ulcers
Diuretics and astringents
Piles, vaginal douches

 DID YOU KNOW?

The ancients dedicated it to the Greek godess Artemis.

The Swedish botanist Carl Linnaeus (1707–78) tells us that horses, sheep and goats eat the plant but cows and pigs dislike its acridity.

As many as 40 per cent of seeds eaten by cattle remain viable after passing through them.

The daisy was also known as Marguerite after the French princess who made it her official emblem.

Shasta daisies were bred from a mix of wild ones, including ox-eye.

Ox-eye daisies now thrive in North America, Australia and New Zealand, too.

MALLOW *Althaea*

Named after Latin *mollis* meaning 'soft' and Greek *althainein*, 'to heal', the mallow spread from European and western Asian origins to stand tall in cottage gardens in Europe and the New World. The superb spikes of pink and white mallow rosettes (similar to related hibiscus and hollyhock) enjoy watery surroundings – salt marshes, inland waterways, riverbanks and ditches. Back in 2,000 BC, Ancient Egyptians were the first to enjoy sticky marshmallow dessert made from the roots – a treat then reserved for gods and royalty.

BEST USES AND CULINARY PARTNERS	
COMPLEMENTS	**CULINARY USES**
Soup: thickens it Salads: finely chop flowers and young leaves	A potherb As a root vegetable (an Ancient Roman delicacy, still popular in Syria) Water left over from cooking any part can be concentrated by boiling and used as an egg-white substitute Tea: from flowers or roots Try boiled and fried with onions and butter

 OILS AND REMEDIES

Its extract is added to creams to treat eczema, dermatitis, boils and abscesses.
Boiled in wine or milk, or given as syrup, it relieves coughs, bronchitis and whooping-cough.
The root makes a skin-softening cosmetic.
The dried root works as a toothbrush or a chew for teething infants.

 DID YOU KNOW?

The 'marshmallow capital' is Ligonier, Indiana, site of an Annual Marshmallow Festival.
30 August is National Toasted Marshmallow Day.
Fibre from the stem and roots is used in paper-making.
Its seed oil is in some paints and varnishes.
The root is used to clean Persian carpets, retaining their vibrant colours.
Mallow's flat, round fruits are called 'cheeses'.
Goats adore eating mallow.
France in the 1800s first saw mallow root sap whipped into a fluffy candy with egg-white meringue and rosewater flavouring.
Today marshmallow sweets are made with gelatin – not marshmallow at all.

 TRADITIONALLY USED FOR

Sore throats, dry coughs
Mouth irritation or soreness
Heartburn, indigestion, colitis, Chron's disease
Preventing perforated stomach ulcers
Excess stomach acid, gastritis
Alimentary canal inflammation
Urinary and respiratory organs
Constipation, dysentery, cystitis
Bruises, sprains, muscle ache
Insect bites, splinters

WATER LILY *Nymphaea*

Water lily flowers last only a few days but their showy, fragrant blooms make the most of their brief appearance with gleaming petals and gorgeous, golden stamens. Some open during the day and some at night; most are pollinated by beetles. Their Latin name derives from fabled water nymphs. Their plate-like leaves float on ponds, marshes and slow-flowing streams, where the cupped flowers rise out of the water. Up to 2,000 seeds are released from each berry-like fruit. Inspired French artist Claude Monet created some 250 water lily oil paintings.

BEST USES AND CULINARY PARTNERS	
COMPLEMENTS	CULINARY USES
Boiled young leaves and unopened buds serve as a vegetable with meats or fish	The seeds, high in protein, starch and oil, may be fried or ground into flour *Nymphaea tuberosa* produce potato-like tubers Native Americans pounded the dried roots to make pancake flour

 OILS AND REMEDIES

Oil from the flowers soothes tumours and eases pain and sores.
Both leaves and flowers make cool compresses.
The leaves calm inflammation.
The syrup is soothing and cooling.
Roots cool, bind, and restrain fluxes.
Good when urine is hot and sharp.
Sweet water lily (*Nymphaea odorata*) root treats dysentery, diarrhoea and gonorrhea.

 TRADITIONALLY USED FOR

Mouth ulcers, sore throats
Boils, tumours, wounds
Sores and inflamed skin
Freckles, sunburn
Ague and raised temperatures
Womb and digestive problems

 DID YOU KNOW?

The Romans thought drinking crushed *Nymphaea* in vinegar for ten days turned a boy into a eunuch.
Giant leaves of Amazon water lilies reach up to about 2 metres (6 feet) across; the flowers are 30 centimetres (1 foot) long.
Lily-trotter birds run across giant lily leaves.

MARIGOLD Pot marigold *Calendula officinalis*

Calendula, meaning little calendar, little clock or little weather-glass, is said to bloom on the *calends* (first day) of every month. Other names include golds, ruddes, corn marigold, marsh marigold, Jackanapes-on-horseback and Mary's gold (after the Virgin Mary). It hails from western Asia and Mediterranean Europe. Romans and Greeks wore ceremonial marigold crowns or garlands and, in India, these sacred flowers decorate Hindu statues. The blooms attract butterflies and bees but their strong odour deters pests, making them excellent companion plants for vegetables.

BEST USES AND CULINARY PARTNERS	
COMPLEMENTS	**CULINARY USES**
Salads	Use petals to make cheese and butter yellow Traditional ingredient in Mediterranean and Middle Eastern dishes Called 'poor man's saffron' The slightly bitter leaves are also edible Dry the peppery-tasting petals for broth and stews

 OILS AND REMEDIES

Only use the common, deep-orange-flowered variety.
The oil is anti-inflammatory, anti-tumour and helps wounds heal.
It is used in soaps, oils, lotions, creams and perfumes.
In American Civil War and World War I battlefields, the antiseptic flowers were used on open wounds and dressings to prevent bleeding and promote healing.
Calendula teas soothe gum and tooth infections, sore throats, tonsillitis and bladder infections.
Calendula succus helps minor surgical incisions heal and prevents infection.

 TRADITIONALLY USED FOR

Wounds, burns, sprains, warts
Inflammation and bleeding
Insect bites, wasp or bee stings
Eczema, acne, skin irritations
Sore eyes, headaches, scrofula
Plague, heart tremors, ague
Stomach ulcers or cramps, constipation
Varicose veins, hemorrhoids
Chapped lips, diaper rash
Smallpox, measles, evil humours
Promoting sneezing and perspiration
Detoxifying liver and gall bladder

 DID YOU KNOW?

Pot marigold is October's birth flower, symbolizing sorrow or sympathy.
If this 'flower of the rains' opens in the morning, rain will follow.
It gives the wearer a vision of whoever robbed him.
Yellow, orange and brown dyes can be extracted and may be used to colour hair.
It is Mexico's flower of the dead.

GOLDENROD *Solidago*

Glowing in open meadows and grasslands, originally from North America and Mexico, the slender rods bear spikes of brilliant yellow flowers. *Solidago* means to make whole or strengthen (after their healing properties) and they are regarded as signalling good fortune – and summer's end. Some produce abundant nectar in balmy weather, attracting bees, wasps and butterflies. Inventor Thomas Edison managed to produce rubber from its leaves and, eventually, car manufacturer Henry Ford presented him with a Model T Ford sporting 'goldenrod' tyres.

BEST USES AND CULINARY PARTNERS	
COMPLEMENTS	**CULINARY USES**
Asparagus, broccoli, cauliflower, cabbage, Brussels sprouts, turnips Mix with allspice	Delicious tea is made from the leaves Goldenrod honey is strong and spicy, getting milder as it matures Use dried, powdered, frozen, pickled or fresh Try in soups, as an egg topping, or in batter Mix with French toast ingredients

 ## OILS AND REMEDIES

Anti-inflammatory *Solidago virgaurea* soothes kidney stones and bladder infections.

Native Americans chewed the leaves or made poultices to relieve sore throats and toothache.

The Cherokee made a tea to soothe bruises plus an insect-sting salve that also healed horse saddle sores.

Boiling the plant produces 'sun medicine', a syrup for colds.

S. ordora seeds have been used as a surgery anaesthetic.

 ## TRADITIONALLY USED FOR

Melancholy, depression
Hayfever, arthritis, diabetes
Internal bleeding, hemorrhoids, sore mouth
Fevers, diarrhoea, fungal infections
Diphtheria, dysentery, intestinal ulcers
Headache, flatulence, vomiting
Dropsy, gout, rheumatism, arthritis
Eczema, asthma, healing wounds
Easing burns and boils

 ## DID YOU KNOW?

A branch held in your hand will nod to indicate where treasure lies.

Woodpeckers peck open the galls and eat the insects inside.

After the Boston Tea Party the colonists drank Goldenrod tea; it became known as Liberty Tea and was exported to China.

Steep flowers and leaves in water to make a yellow dye.

Wear a sprig and you will see your future sweetheart tomorrow.

Goldenrod springing up by your door marks the arrival of good fortune.

A patch in the woods heralds an underground spring.

The bruised leaves smell like carrot.

HIBISCUS *Malvaceae*

The beautiful, exotic rose mallow or hibiscus originated in subtropical and tropical regions but grows happily in temperate climes and is much prized for its superb blooms that attract butterflies, bees and hummingbirds. It spread from Angola to flourish in China, Egypt, Mexico, Sudan, Thailand and elsewhere. Philippine children crush the flowers and leaves to extract the sticky juice; hollow stalks are dipped into this and used as straws for blowing hibiscus bubbles.

BEST USES AND CULINARY PARTNERS	
COMPLEMENTS	CULINARY USES
Sugar, honey, cinnamon, ginger Lemon balm and St John's wort in a soothing tea	The tea is popular in Iraq, Iran, Latin America, the Philippines, Jamaica, Barbados, Trinidad and Tobago, Levant, Egypt, Sudan, Italy, Russia and the USA It is called red sorrel in the Caribbean, Jamaica in the USA, sour tea in Iran West Sudanese often serve white hibiscus tea Dried hibiscus is a Mexican delicacy It can be candied as a garnish

 OILS AND REMEDIES

Hibiscus rosa-sinensis flower extracts absorb ultra-violet radiation and may act as anti-solar agents.
In India the roots are used in cough medicines and to prevent hair loss or greying.
Leaves and flowers ground into a soapy paste serve as a conditioning shampoo.
Tart hibiscus tea contains vitamin C.

 TRADITIONALLY USED FOR

Temperature and fluid balance
Lowering blood pressure
Improving cardiovascular health
Maintaining (or lowering) cholesterol levels
Good circulation and respiratory health
Throat and skin problems
Insomnia, constipation
Deep-red hibiscus tea is a diuretic

? DID YOU KNOW?

It is the national or state flower of Haiti, Hawaii, South Korea and Malaysia.
Tahitan and Hawaiian girls wear the flower in their hair: if worn on the right, the girl is single or available for a relationship; a left placement means she is spoken for!
It can make a red food colouring.
The Hindu goddess Kali may be depicted with a red hibiscus: the flower is often offered to Kali and Lord Ganesha.
Hibiscus cannabinus is used in papermaking.

MYRTLE *Myrtus communis* and *Myrtus nivellei*

Symbolic of love, immortality and the Garden of Eden, myrtle (*Myrtus communis*) scents Europe's Mediterranean region, especially Corsica and Sardinia. White or pink, star-like flowers are followed by round, blue-black or amber berries – beloved by birds. Saharan myrtle (*Myrtus nivellei*) flourishes in the barren mountains of Algeria and Chad and in sparse woodland above the desert plains. Myrtle was sacred to the Roman goddess Venus and women bathed in myrtle-scented water, wearing myrtle crowns. It featured in Roman gardens and was reintroduced in the 1500s by Sir Walter Raleigh and Sir Francis Carey. By the 1700s potted myrtles were being overwintered indoors and brought outside to blossom in summer. A phallic symbol, its branches were presented to bridegrooms and appear in wedding bouquets and Ukrainian wedding crowns.

BEST USES AND CULINARY PARTNERS	
COMPLEMENTS	CULINARY USES
Marinades and soups with its spicy, citrusy flavour Leaves taste like allspice with menthol Leaves and berries season lamb and pork.	In Corsica and Sardinia myrtle is used in an aromatic liqueur called *Mirto* The berries serve as a pepper substitute Flowers serve as a garnish

 OILS AND REMEDIES

The essential oil alleviates acne and skin diseases.
Herbal teas made from dried leaves and berries lower
diabetic blood-glucose levels.
May have anticancer, anti-inflammatory and
antioxidant properties.
Tuareg people use it as a traditional medicine.
The leaves were used in ritual washing of the dead.

 TRADITIONALLY USED FOR

Sinus
Urinary and bladder infections
Alzheimer's disease
To lower cholesterol

 DID YOU KNOW?

A myrtle cutting from Queen Victoria's wedding bouquet
took root; its sprigs have been used in the royal wedding
bouquets of Queen Elizabeth II, Diana, Princess of Wales,
and Kate Middleton, Duchess of Cambridge.
In the Botticelli painting, Venus, goddess of love, is showered
with myrtle as she rises from the ocean.
Myrtle is a character in *The Great Gatsby* by F. Scott Fitzgerald.
Moaning Myrtle appears in the Harry Potter series by J. K.
Rowling.

PYRETHRUM *Chrysanthemum coccineum* and *Tanacetum cinerariifolium*

Part of the daisy family, pyrethrums vary in colour from pink, white, red or purple (painted daisies or Persian chrysanthemums) to white with yellow centres (Dalmatian chrysanthemums). All have fernlike foliage. *C. coccineum* is grown as an insecticide, as the pyrethrin chemicals they contain repel insects by attacking their nervous systems, even inhibiting mosquitoes from biting. Pyrethrum daisies were first recorded 2,000 years ago during China's Chou Dynasty when it was traded along the Silk Route and eventually grown in the Dalmatian region. French soldiers crushed the flowers to control fleas and body lice during the Napoleonic Wars.

 ## OILS AND REMEDIES

Apply directly to the skin as an insecticide
It kills pests and is biodegradable, rapidly disintegrating in sunlight

 ## TRADITIONALLY USED FOR

Repelling:
Cockroaches, yellowjackets, ants
Wasps, thrips, fleas, bedbugs
Head lice, crab lice and their nits
Mites (scabies)

 ## CULTIVATION HISTORY

1860: Pyrethrum powder introduced to USA.
1881: Cultivation reaches Japan.
1914: Japan becomes main supplier to USA.
1928: Cultivation reaches Kenya where most potent flowers now grow.
Croatia and Japan also supply potent flowers.
1932: Full commercial production begins.
1975: 23,000 tons harvested in Kenya.
1998: Kenya supplies 90 per cent of world's pyrethrum.
Today: Tasmania produces 60 per cent of global crop.

 ## DID YOU KNOW?

Planting pyrethrums in the vegetable garden limits damage from insects and browsing animals.
Pyrethrins are called py for short.
They are amongst the safest insecticides to use near food.
Pyrethrum contains six distinct insecticidal pyrethrins.

WARNING

Pyrethrins can trigger life-threatening allergic responses including heart failure and severe asthma not to mention headaches, dizziness and difficulty breathing
They are extremely toxic to bees and fish
Although not always deadly to mammals, they should be kept away from pets
Pyrethrum can be safely sprayed on vegetables and fruit – so long as these are not picked for 48 hours
It should not be used by those sensitive to ragweed

BALSAM *Impatiens*

There are about 1,000 species of *Impatiens*, ranging from jewel-like, tiny flowers to 2-metre (7-feet), reed-like giants. Some, like Himalayan balsam (*I. glandulifera*), are highly invasive, with seedpods that explode, broadcasting up to 800 seeds over a wide area. Common names include jewelweed, touch-me-not, snapweed and Busy Lizzie. They enjoy moist and rich soils, reed beds, riverbanks, roadside ditches and forest edges, where they attract moth and butterfly larvae, bumblebees and beetles – but their leaves are toxic to birds such as budgerigars who eat only the flowers.

BEST USES AND CULINARY PARTNERS	
COMPLEMENTS	**CULINARY USES**
Cakes, breads and biscuits	Nutty, so use like hazelnuts or walnuts
	Immature seed pods can be cooked like mangetout and are used in stirfries and curries
	Seeds can be toasted and ground to make flour, spice or ground-almond substitute
	Seeds make a fine addition to stews and curries
	Flowers and seeds can be used in floral jams, jellies, vinegar and marzipan

 TRADITIONALLY USED FOR

Bee stings and other insect bites
Stinging nettle rashes
Poison-ivy contact dermatitis
Acute anxiety and stress

 OILS AND REMEDIES

Impatiens is one of the 38 plants used for Bach herbal remedies.
Its flower extracts are included in the Bach Five Flower Remedy.
Himalayan balsam (*Impatiens glandulifera*) seeds have been eaten in India for centuries.

DID YOU KNOW?

They are sometimes called Policeman's Helmet because that is what the flower shape resembles.
Impatiens means 'impatient' and refers to the way the ripe seedpods of *I. glandulifera* 'explode', shooting seeds up to 7 metres (22 feet) away.
Certain jewelweeds contain a dye like henna that colours hair or skin.
The petals mashed with alum, rose and orchid petals served as a manicure polish in China, very slowly turning nails reddish pink.

 WARNING

Some varieties are slightly toxic and can cause vomiting and diarrhoea.

BORAGE *Borago officinalis*

Also called starflower or bugloss, borage is a Mediterranean plant, long grown in kitchen gardens for its edible leaves and pretty blue flowers, which yield sweet honey. The leaves can be boiled as a potherb or eaten young in salads, while its seeds make oil. It is a vegetable in Crete and parts of Spain (boiled and sautéed with garlic). In Italy it often serves as a pasta filling. A companion plant, it may protect legumes, spinach, brassicas, strawberries and tomatoes.

BEST USES AND CULINARY PARTNERS		
FLAVOURS AND TASTES	**COMBINES WITH**	**CULINARY USES**
Fresh borage smells and tastes like cucumber	Cider Claret cups Polish pickles	The vibrant edible flowers decorate desserts Flowers can be preserved and candied Leaves and flowers are often popped into Pimms cocktails Was added to gin before cucumber became fashionable Borage Grüne Soße (green sauce) is made in Frankfurt, Germany

 ## TRADITIONALLY USED FOR

Gastrointestinal and cardiovascular issues
Respiratory problems, asthma, bronchitis
Sore throat, colic, cramps, diarrhoea
Urinary, kidney or bladder ailments
Regulating metabolism and hormones
PMS, menopause, hot flushes
Hypochondria, rheumatism
Putrid and pestilential fever
Venom of serpents
Jaundice, consumption

 ## OILS AND REMEDIES

The flower syrup relieves depression.
It drives away '*...sadnesse, dulnesse and melancholy*' (John Gerald, 1597).
In Iran, borage tea relieves colds, flu, bronchitis and arthritis.
Its seeds make oil.

 ## DID YOU KNOW?

Borage-flavoured wine was drunk by Celtic warriors to bolster their courage before battle.
Borage may have been the 'Nepenthe' written about by ancient Greek poet Homer, which, steeped in wine, banished pain, woe and sad memories.
The name may have come from the Celtic word *borrach* meaning courage, or from the Latin *burra* (wool flock), perhaps inspired by its thick covering of short hairs.
The Welsh name translates as 'herb of gladness'.

GENTIAN *Gentiana*

Clinging to mountains including the Alps, Andes and Himalayas, these dazzling alpine gems range from just a few centimeters high to two-metre giants (six and a half feet). Although predominantly radiant blue, they are mainly white in New Zealand and red in the Andes (here pollinated by birds) – with a further scattering of yellow, purple, mauve and green varieties. Bees flock to their azure trumpets. The name derives from Gentius, a king of Illyria around 180 BC, who was said to have discovered gentian as a plague remedy and tonic. It has also served as a poison antidote.

BEST USES AND CULINARY PARTNERS	
COMPLEMENTS	CULINARY USES
Aperitifs, tonics and bitters Yellow *Gentiana lutea* flavours liqueurs	Beverages are made with the roots *Gentian* is a distilled Alpine speciality In the 1700s gentian wine was a pre-dinner aperitif

 ## OILS AND REMEDIES

Root, bark and leaves are used.

Gentian is used in Bach flower remedies; *Gentiana lutea* and *Gentiana punctata* are especially useful.

The herb steeped in wine refreshes weary travellers.

Combined with elderflower, verbena and cowslip, it relieves sinusitis.

Culpeper stated that gentian 'prevent[s] the pestilence ... comforts the heart and preserves it against faintings and swoonings ... helps the biting of mad dogs and venomous beasts.'

 ## TRADITIONALLY USED FOR

Hysteria

Parasitic worms, wounds, bruises, cancer

Gout, lame joints, rheumatism, arthritis

Indigestion, heartburn, stitches, muscle spasms

Gassiness, diarrhoea, vomiting

High blood pressure

Liver and spleen disorders

Fever, flu, malaria, jaundice

Loss of appetite and exhaustion

Promoting menstruation

 ## DID YOU KNOW?

In romantic novels Gentian is a popular name for heroines – and pirates!

The flowers are a source of blue dye.

Before the introduction of hops, gentian was used in brewing.

The medieval Hungarian monarch, Saint Ladislas, asked God to show him a plague cure, then fired an arrow that pierced a gentian root.

SPEEDWELL *Veronica*

Because its petals fall so quickly, the plant was given the name speedwell, which is a short form of the phrase 'Farewell, Godspeed, may you speed well and thrive'. Its Latin name derives from the story of Saint Veronica, who gave Jesus her veil to wipe His face on the road to Calvary; the cloth retained Christ's image while the flower's petal markings remind us of His blood and tears. There are some 500 species, ranging from low, dense clusters of sweet violet-blue flowers to tall, spiked, white, blue, pink or purple mint-like plants. All thrive in gravelly soils, attracting butterflies and humming birds. Europe and western Asia's *Veronica officinalis* is also called heath speedwell, common speedwell, gypsyweed and Paul's betony. When the Romans conquered the Germanic Teutons, they discovered medicinal speedwell and took it further across Europe.

BEST USES AND CULINARY PARTNERS		
FLAVOURS AND TASTES	**COMPLEMENTS**	**CULINARY USES**
Nutritious *Veronica americana* tastes like watercress	Soup and salads Nettle tea	Makes a good green tea substitute with sage and wood betony (in France called European tea)

 OILS AND REMEDIES

This cure-all is dubbed 'the herb for survival'; it is said to cure everything from colds to gall stones.
It is used in body tonics, syrups, elixirs, sunscreen, moisturizers and hair products.
Rich in vitamins and tannins, it is anti-inflammatory.
As a bitter tea made with stinging-nettle tops, it cleanses the blood and soothes flaky, irritated skin.

 DID YOU KNOW?

It was claimed to repel witches, demons and devils.
A stylized speedwell features on Britain's RAF Squadron 541 badge.
It was a Roman compliment to say someone had as many good qualities as the herb speedwell.
In Ireland, wearing a veronica spray is said to keep a traveller safe.
Native Americans used it in a tea.

 TRADITIONALLY USED FOR

Nervous system disorders, mental exhaustion, improving memory
Coughs, respiratory tract problems, bronchial congestion, asthma
Skin complaints, eczema
Sinus and ear infections
Gastrointestinal distress, stimulating digestive juices
Bladder gravel
Lowering cholesterol
Rheumatism, gout
Allergies
Liver, spleen, cardiovascular system
Leprosy

CHICORY *Cichorium intybus*

Native to western Asia, North Africa and Europe, chicory has been enjoyed since Ancient Egyptians, Greeks and medieval monks cultivated it. With its clear azure flowers, it is called blue dandelion, blue daisy, blue sailors and blue weed (as well as cornflower, coffee-weed, horseweed, ragged sailors, succory, wild bachelor's buttons and wild endive). European folklore claimed that chicory could open locked doors.

BEST USES AND CULINARY PARTNERS	
COMPLEMENTS	**CULINARY USES**
Salad mixes Yoghurt Fish and steak as a side vegetable Fava bean purée Boiled and sautéed leaves with pasta or meat dishes	Use bitter leaves and blanched buds for salad Serve as a spinach substitute, simmered and marinated in olive oil *Puntarelle* (popular in Rome) is made with chicory sprouts Some beer brewers use roasted chicory to flavour stout and strong blond ales As a food sweetener

 OILS AND REMEDIES

Chicory was used in Ancient Greek medicine.
It is an excellent source of potassium, folate and vitamins A and C.
Root chicory contains volatile oils.
Chicory flower was a popular folk medicine and tonic in Germany.
It is one of the 38 Bach flower remedies.
Chicory-leaf compresses ease skin inflammation and swellings.

 TRADITIONALLY USED FOR

Gallstones, spleen problems
Worms, intestinal parasites
Loss of appetite, gastro-enteritis, jaundice
Constipation, bowels
Cuts and bruises
Sedation
Rheumatism, gout
Sinus problems
Hormone balance, PMS symptoms
Ague, St Anthony's fire

? DID YOU KNOW?

Chicory is closely linked to coffee. The roots serve as a fine coffee substitute or additive, and the Dutch have always added chicory to coffee.
Chicory coffee was drunk by Confederate soldiers during the American Civil War and it is still served to prisoners in the USA.
Chicory eked out scant coffee reserves during the 1930s Great Depression and World War II.
Camp Coffee, marketed from 1885, includes chicory essence.
Chicory is a fine oat substitute and de-worms farm animals.
It may grow 1.5 metres (5 feet) high.
Ancient Egyptians believed it purified the blood and liver.
Culpepper recommended it for swooning and passions of the heart.

CENTAURY Common or European *Centaurium erythraea*

This European, western Asian and North African herb is also called minor centaury, feverwort, filwort, bitter herb, red centaury, Christ's ladder or centaury gentian. Growing from a small basal rosette, it has petite, light pink, lavender or red flowers that open with the sunrise and shut towards sunset. It thrives in boggy meadows but also on turfy sea-cliffs and dry dunes. It is named after the centaurs of Greek mythology, one of whom, Chiron, was a skilled herbalist who used the herb to heal wounds. Centaury was said to be powerful against wicked spirits.

BEST USES AND CULINARY PARTNERS	
COMPLEMENTS	**CULINARY USES**
Gives a strong, bitter flavour to many beverages Tonics and apertifs Pastis	Infused in hot water to quench thirst As a herbal tea Centaury wine

 OILS AND REMEDIES

Centaury was recommended by Hippocrates as an excellent antiseptic tonic.

The aromatic tea helps patients with gastric and liver diseases.

The herb was used in Portland Powder, a famous gout remedy.

Mixed with a little honey the juice helps to clear the eyes 'from dimness, mists and clouds'.

 TRADITIONALLY USED FOR

Worms, body vermin, head lice, snakebites
Jaundice, dropsy
Freckles, spots, marks
Ulcers and wounds
Bloating, dyspepsia, heartburn, flatulence, constipation
Anorexia, loss of appetite
Rheumatism
Sedation
Fever
Stimulating appetite, improving digestion

 DID YOU KNOW?

Centaury was one of the fifteen magical herbs of the Ancient Britons.

In Worcestershire, England, it is known as Centre of the Sun.

Saxon herbalists used its juice for poisons, snakebites, and to cure intermittent fevers, hence its name, feverwort.

The Romans named it Gall of the Earth, after its extreme bitterness.

If put in a fire on a starlit night, it was said to make the stars appear to fight.

If mixed with female lapwing (black plover) blood, and lit with oil in a lamp, it might make those nearby believe themselves to be witches.

VIPER'S BUGLOSS *Echium vulgare*

The scientific name of this plant comes from the Greek *echis* meaning 'viper'; its red stamens flick like tongues, while speckled stalks and pointed seeds resemble snakes' heads. Bugloss (also of Greek origin), means an ox or cow's tongue – inspired by the plant's rough, tongue-shaped leaves. It is also called adderwort, bluebottle, Our Saviour's Flannel, blueweed, blue-devil, blue thistle and ironweed. The flowers begin rosy pink and turn vivid blue. Covered with prickly hairs, it thrives in dry grassland, walls, quarries, gravel pits, cliffs, banks, dunes and shingle. It is beloved of burnet moths, butterflies like the painted lady and large skipper, hoverflies, buff-tailed and red-tailed bumblebees, honeybees and red mason bees.

 ## OILS AND REMEDIES

An expellent of poisons and venom, it is said to cure viper bites.
It may be used externally on unbroken skin.
The leaves, especially those near the root, make an excellent cordial or infusion, which encourages perspiration, alleviating fevers and inflammatory pains.
A decoction of the seeds in wine drives away melancholy.

 ## TRADITIONALLY USED FOR

Insect bites
Adder bites
Fever
Headaches
Nervous complaints
Passions and heart-trembling
Swoonings, sadness, melancholy

 ## DID YOU KNOW?

Artists use the burned root to draw, like charcoal.
It is grown as an oilseed crop.
The sharp stem hairs puncture skin and cause dermatitis.
In China its name means 'blue luck'.
In Austria its name means 'sky-fire' or 'proud Heinrich'.

 WARNING
The plant is potentially toxic – it can cause irreparable liver damage.
However, a few drops – taken short term – may alleviate certain acute conditions.

FLAX OR LINSEED *Linum*

Flax has delicate, pale-blue or turquoise flowers. Linseed is the source of one of the earliest commercial oils – generally applied externally but sometimes taken internally (do check instructions carefully and confer with a doctor if taking other medication). Traces of spun, dyed flax fibres date back 30,000 years; it was certainly a crop in Switzerland, Germany, China and India 5,000 years ago and Christ's body was wrapped in linen (the cloth made from flax), as were Egyptian mummies. The plant has been used for numerous purposes, including lamp-wicks, rope, sailcloth, canvas, cigarette and bank note paper, teabags and linoleum. Flanders became the major linen producer in the Middle Ages when the flowers were said to protect against sorcery. Ultimately, the rise of cotton and synthetic fibres diminished its status.

BEST USES AND CULINARY PARTNERS	
COMPLEMENTS	**CULINARY USES**
Breakfast cereals and oatmeal Salads, eggs, fish, meats	Flax seed sprouts are edible, with a slightly spicy, nutty flavor. In northern India, flax seed is roasted, powdered and eaten with boiled rice.

 OILS AND REMEDIES

Flax seeds may lower cholesterol levels.
Crushed linseed-meal poultices allay irritation and pain, and promote suppuration.
Linseed tea (with honey and lemon juice) soothes colds, coughs and urinary organ irritation.

 TRADITIONALLY USED FOR

Lowering blood pressure
Respiratory disorders, coughs, pleurisy
Burns, scalds, abscesses, boils
Infections, cold, flu, fever
Eyes
Rheumatism, gout
Breast and prostrate cancers
Gravel and stone, constipation

 DID YOU KNOW?

The Germanic goddess Hulda first taught mortals the art of spinning and weaving flax.
Ancient Greek and Roman linseed bread caused flatulence.
Bohemians say that if seven-year-old children dance among flax, they grow beautiful.
Bundles of flax fibre look like blonde hair, hence *flaxen* locks.
In early versions of *Sleeping Beauty*, the princess pricks her finger on a flax sliver – later sucked out by children conceived as she slept.
Flax fibres are twice as strong as cotton, making it popular for everything from bandages to bedlinen.
Ground linseed has been used by cheats to adulterate the more expensive ingredient pepper.
The plant has been used for paints, varnish and printing inks.

WARNING

 Eat the seed, only. Ingesting the plant or oil in large quantities can lead to bowel obstruction, breathing problems, convulsions or paralysis
Skin contact with linseed oil may cause minor irritation.

PHEASANT'S EYE *Adonis autumnalis, vernalis* and *annua*

The Latin name derives from the legend of Adonis, god of beauty and desire; the flower sprang from his blood when he was killed by a wild boar. Bright yellow *Adonis vernalis* is called spring (or yellow) pheasant's eye and false hellebore; scarlet and orange-flowered varieties with dark stamens are dubbed red Morocco pheasant's eye, red mathes, blooddrops, red chamomile, rose-a-ruby, soldiers-in-green and sweet vernal. Their graceful anemone-like cups blaze on dry meadows, cornfield margins, rocky slopes and roadsides from the steppes of North Africa and Eurasia (especially the Crimea), to Siberia and Labrador. They are pollinated by bees, flies and beetles.

 OILS AND REMEDIES

Like foxglove (digitalis), *Adonis vernalis* contains cardiac glycosides.

It impacts like digitalis but is about ten times as powerful and acts faster.

It improves heart efficiency, increasing output but slowing heart rate.

It stimulates heart muscles and causes contraction of the smaller arteries, thus increasing arterial tension.

It has a sedative action and helps when hearts are beating too fast or irregularly.

It diminishes pulse frequency and regulates heart-beat.

It may succeed where digitalis fails, especially for kidney disease .

Even marginal overdosing causes vomiting and diarrhoea.

It is included in many proprietary medicines.

Its effects are *not* cumulative.

 DID YOU KNOW?

Pheasant's eye was introduced as a cardiac stimulant in Russia in 1879 by a Dr Bubnow, who had observed Russian peasants using it for dropsy and heart disease.

Its namesake gamebirds also have red eyes.

The seedpods resemble loganberries or little corn-cobs.

 TRADITIONALLY USED FOR

Should be administered only by qualified medical practitioners

Low blood pressure

Heart disease, angina, cardiac dropsy

Bright's disease heart issues

Cramps, palpitations, fever

Kidney disease, diarrhoea

Menstrual disorders

Water retention

 WARNING

This is a poison, albeit used in medicine with appropriate caution.

Large doses paralyze both heart and blood vessels.

It can kill grazing horses and pigs.

TANSY *Tanacetum vulgare*

Native to Asia and Europe and used in Ancient Greek medicine, bitter, aromatic tansy has clusters of yellow, button-like flowers and smells of camphor. Its leaves once served as a bittering agent for home-brewed beer and as a pungent strew over Tudor castle floors. Also known as bitter buttons, cow bitter, mugwort or golden buttons, it was cultivated in Charlemagne's herb gardens and by Benedictine monks in Switzerland. During Lent, Christians served tansy cakes to remind them of the bitter herbs consumed by the Israelites – and to control flatulence after eating copious pulses!

BEST USES AND CULINARY PARTNERS	
COMPLEMENTS	**CULINARY USES**
Omelettes Tennessee whiskey Peppermint	Tansy seeds were used in funeral biscuits A bittering agent for beer

 ## OILS AND REMEDIES

Tansy tea helps expel worms.

In the Middle Ages, large doses induced abortions. But it has also been used to help conception and prevent miscarriages.

The oil includes camphor, used in lacquers, varnishes, explosives, rubs and mothballs.

It cools, lightens and purifies skin, soothing itching and pain.

An insect repellant, tansy was worn in shoes to prevent fevers and malaria, rubbed into meat to prolong storage, placed in bed linen to repel fleas and by windows to deter flies and ants.

It is an antibacterial in root canal dental work.

Worm-repelling tansy has been used for embalming corpses and has been packed into coffins and funeral winding sheets.

 ## TRADITIONALLY USED FOR

Rheumatism, gout, joint pain
Indigestion, wind, weak kidneys
Fevers, colds, jaundice, chest rubs
Migraine, hysteria
Herpes, sores,
Sprains, wounds, swelling
Repelling mosquitoes and ticks, intestinal worms
'Bringing out' measles

 ## DID YOU KNOW?

It is planted next to potatoes to repel Colorado beetles. As a companion plant, tansy repels ants, beetles and squash bugs.

Some insects (like *Chrysolina graminis* beetle) resist its toxins and survive almost exclusively on tansy.

Tansy makes a golden dye.

The dried flowers work well in floral arrangements.

Jack Daniel, of the Tennessee whiskey fame, enjoyed adding sugar and crushed tansy leaf to his own drink.

 ## WARNING

The volatile oil contains toxins that can cause convulsions or liver and brain damage.

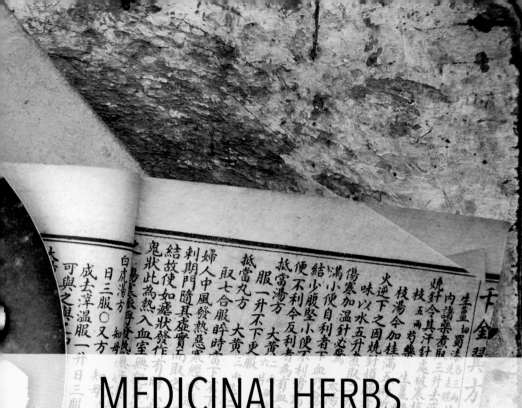

MEDICINAL HERBS

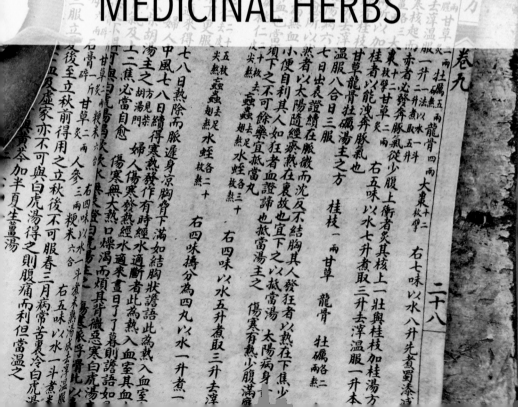

千金翼方　卷九

二十八

右七味以水八升先煮蜀漆減二升內諸藥煮取三升去滓溫服一升　甘草燒針令其汗針處被寒核起而赤者必發奔豚氣從少腹上衝心者灸其核上各一壯與桂枝加桂湯方

桂枝五兩　芍藥　生薑各三兩　甘草二兩炙　大棗十二枚擘

右五味以水七升煮取三升去滓溫服一升本云桂枝湯今加桂滿五兩所以加桂者以能洩奔豚氣也

火逆下之因燒針煩躁者桂枝甘草龍骨牡蠣湯主之方

桂枝一兩　甘草　龍骨　牡蠣各二熬

右四味以水五升煮取三升去滓溫服八合日三服

傷寒脈浮醫以火迫劫之亡陽必驚狂起臥不安者桂枝去芍藥加蜀漆牡蠣龍骨救逆湯主之方

抵當湯方
大黃三兩　桃仁二十枚　水蛭　虻蟲各三十熬
右四味以水五升煮取三升去滓溫服一升不下更服

抵當丸方
大黃三兩　桃仁二十五枚　水蛭　虻蟲各二十熬
右四味擣分為四丸以水一升煮一丸取七合服睟時當下血若不下者更服

太陽病身黃脈沈結少腹鞕小便不利者為無血也小便自利其人如狂者血證諦也抵當湯主之

傷寒有熱少腹滿應小便不利今反利者為有血也當下之不可餘藥宜抵當丸方

婦人中風發熱惡寒經水適來得之七八日熱除而脈遲身涼胸脅下滿如結胸狀譫語者此為熱入血室其血必結故使如瘧狀發作有時小柴胡湯主之方

婦人傷寒發熱經水適來晝日明了暮則譫語如見鬼狀者此為熱入血室無犯胃氣及上二焦必自愈

婦人中風七八日續得寒熱發作有時經水適斷者此為熱入血室其血必結故使如瘧狀發作有時小柴胡湯主之方

成去滓溫服一升日三服○又方　知母六兩　石膏一斤碎　甘草二兩炙　粳米六合　人參三兩

右五味以水一斗煮米熟湯成去滓溫服一升日三服

此方立夏後至立秋前得服之立秋後不可服正月二月三月尚凜冷亦不可與之與之則嘔利而腹痛諸亡血虛家亦不可與得之則腹痛而利但可溫之及汗後亦不可與也不渴者不與白虎湯凡用白虎湯得之則腹痛而利但當溫之

黃芩加半夏生薑湯

DANDELION *Taraxacum officinale*

Dandelions spread over meadows, wasteland and gardens. About 93 insect types transfer its pollen until its fluffy plumed seeds disperse in the breeze – or when children puff at the dandelion 'clock'. Its name 'dent de lion' means lion's tooth – after its toothed leaves or golden 'lion's mane' of petals. When these close, it is also called swine's snout and, as winds snatch its white 'hair' away, priest's crown. Vulgarly termed 'piss-a-beds', this attribute still permeates children's playground lore – with justification, as dandelion has long been used as a diuretic to release excess fluids.

BEST USES AND CULINARY PARTNERS	
COMPLEMENTS	CULINARY USES
Young leaves are good in salads and vegetable soups Grate or chop roots to mix with salad leaves Fry with onions, garlic (and perhaps wine) in olive oil	Tastes like chicory and endive, with a bitter tinge Serve raw or boiled like spinach Its roasted roots make a coffee Its flowers make wine Try dandelion tea, beer, tonic and stout

 ## OILS AND REMEDIES

Roots and stems are filled with a white, milky bitter juice – a powerful herbal medicine.
The plants are full of vitamins A, B, C and D plus iron, potassium and zinc.

 ## DID YOU KNOW?

Arabian physicians in the 900s used dandelion.
Dandelions were part of Welsh medicines in the 1200s.
Native Americans boiled dandelion water to treat kidney disease, swelling, skin, heartburn and upset stomachs.
In traditional Chinese medicine, it eased stomach problems, appendicitis and breast inflammation.
Small birds eat the seeds.
Rabbits and hens love the leaves.
Pigs and goats devour the entire plant.
Dandelion flowers make a green-yellow dye; the roots make a brown dye.
The seeds may fly 8 kilometres (5 miles) away.

 ## TRADITIONALLY USED FOR

Liver, kidney and eye problems
Fever, boils, sores
Diabetes, diarrhoea, upset stomachs
High blood pressure
Stimulating appetite
Detoxifying liver and gallbladder
Improving immune systems
Normalizing blood sugar levels
Lowering 'bad' cholesterol
Ague fits, pestilential fevers

CHAMOMILE *Matricaria chamomilla, Matricaria recutita*
Chamaemelum nobile, Anthemis mixta

Found in Europe, Asia and North Africa, chamomile has a sweet, crisp, fruity fragrance and silver-white flowers with golden centres. Mentioned in the Ebers Papyrus and used from 1550 BC in Egypt to embalm the dead, relieve ague and cure the sick, it was dedicated to the sun god Ra. Later, the Greeks (who called it 'ground-apple') and Romans both recommended chamomile; by the Middle Ages it was cultivated by monks and as a domestic garden herb. Also called scented mayweed, it has a distinct apple aroma and, in Tudor times, served as an aromatic strewing herb. It is used in cosmetics and perfumes, grown in lawns (as at Buckingham Palace) and planted in garden walks.

BEST USES AND CULINARY PARTNERS	
COMPLEMENTS	**CULINARY USES**
Combines well with lemon, honey and vanilla	Spaniards call it *manzanilla* (little apple) and add it to their lightest sherries It is good for herb beers It flavours herbal teas

 ## OILS AND REMEDIES

Medieval alchemists distilled essential oil from chamomile.
It is used in aromatherapy to reduce stress, moisturize skin and promote sleep.
Chamomile extracts may inhibit cancer cell growth in skin, prostate, breast, ovaries and prostate; they also slow the growth of polio and herpes viruses plus bacteria like streptococcus.
It reduces facial swellings caused by abscesses.
Chamomile flowers emit a deeply relaxing aroma and are put in 'dream pillows'.

 ## TRADITIONALLY USED FOR

Hay fever, allergies, inflammation, rashes
Muscle spasm, cramping, sprains
Gastrointestinal and menstrual pain
Indigestion, appetite loss, stomachache
Ulcers, hemorrhoids, constipation
Urinary infections, insomnia
Toothache, earache, migraine, neuralgia
Hysterical and nervous affections
Nightmare, anxiety, delirium tremens
Heartburn, gout, ague, colic
Jaundice, dropsy, respiratory pain

 ## DID YOU KNOW?

English flowerheads are best for oil distillation.
German/Hungarian chamomile is called blue chamomile.
Chamomile oil in a warm bath soothes away stress.
Chamomile will dye fabrics yellow and enhance blonde hair.
Chamomile heals neighbouring sick plants.
It was an important ingredient of mummification embalming oil.
The Romans used it to make incense and beverages.

CLOVER OR TREFOIL *Trifolium pretense*

Clover, a main source of nectar for honeybees, flourishes worldwide, even in the Arctic Circle and on high mountain slopes. Symbolic of earth, sea and sky to druids and a Celtic sacred magical plant, it was a charm to ward off evil spirits and witches. The Irish shamrock is associated with St Patrick's teaching of the Holy Trinity (Father, Son and Holy Spirit); its three leaves also represent faith, hope and love. Any fourth leaf stands for stunning good luck, of course! Clovers symbolized a prosperous, joyous marriage and protected sweethearts; no bride should go down the aisle without clovers in both shoes!

BEST USES AND CULINARY PARTNERS	
COMPLEMENTS	CULINARY USES
Salads and teas	The petals have a sweet taste Add tiny florets to summer iced mint tea – or to decorate cake icing

 OILS AND REMEDIES

Wild red clover serves as a tonic tea or skin wash.
It is an ingredient in liniments and balms.
It contains blood-thinning coumarin.
It stimulates the iimmune system.

 TRADITIONALLY USED FOR

Sickness, gout, diabetes, AIDS
Coughs, whooping cough, respiratory congestion
Thrombosis, thinning blood
Cancers (skin, breast, ovaries, lymph glands)
Sores, burns, eczema

 DID YOU KNOW?

Trefoil derives from *tres* (three) and *folium* (leaf).
Red clover, high in vegetable protein, is a valuable forage
   crop that fattens cattle.
'Being in clover' means to lead an easy comfortable life.
Traditionally, a two-leaf clover enabled young maidens to see
   their future lovers.
Legends claim that Eve took a four-leaf clover with her from
   the Garden of Eden. This had great power against evil – to
   deter snakes, witches and the devil – while bestowing
   second sight and the ability to see fairies.
A four-leaf clover brings luck to lovers; discovering one means
   that you will soon find your true soul mate.
A five-leafed clover betokens a good marriage, but witches
   wore five-leafed ones to boost their evil powers.

FEVERFEW *Tanacetum parthenium*

Also called *feather*few, febrifuge and bachelor's buttons, feverfew first raised its small, daisy-like heads in the Balkan peninsula, Anatolia and the Caucasus but then spread through Europe, North America and Chile. The name reflects its former role as a fever reducer and it was noted in the first century AD as an anti-inflammatory by the Greek Dioscorides. It also prevents migraines. With jewel-like yellow centres, white outer rays, citrus-scented leaves and hairy stems, it is happy in hedgerows, roadsides and woodland borders – and has a strong bitter smell, disliked by bees.

 OILS AND REMEDIES

Despite its name, feverfew does *not* work very well in fever reduction but *has* proved a popular migraine treatment. In the 1980s a survey of migraine sufferers showed that 70 per cent of participants improved after taking two to three fresh feverfew leaves daily; those suffering chronic migraines noted fewer occurrences.

A decoction with sugar or honey soothes coughs.

Bruise and heat, fry with oil and wine and apply externally while warm to soothe wind and colic.

A tincture applied locally instantly relieves insect bites.

Use in drinks (or bound on the wrists) to ease ague.

 DID YOU KNOW?

Planted round dwellings, feverfew purifies the atmosphere and wards off disease.

In medieval days, it was said to protect against plague and mad-dog bites.

Seventeenth-century herbalist John Parkinson advised that feverfew sped up recovery from an opium overdose.

Fresh stems and leaves make a yellow-light green dye.

 TRADITIONALLY USED FOR

Migraine and headaches

Hysteria, nervousness, low spirits

Face-ache, neuralgia, earache

Coughs, wheezing, difficulty breathing

Hayfever, nausea, vomiting

Wind, colic, digestive problems

Insect and vermin bites

Arthritis, sciatica

Childbirth, labour, expelling placenta

Menstrual cramps, promoting periodic flow

Alcoholic delirium tremens

Intestinal worms, malaria

 WARNING

Treat with caution: It serves as a general tonic but can cause withdrawal and allergic reactions and should not be taken by pregnant women. It may interact with blood-thinners and medications metabolized by the liver.

NETTLE *Urtica dioca*

With heart-shaped, serrated leaves and tiny flowers, most nettles (also called burn nettle, burn weed, and burn hazel) are covered with stiff hairs that act like tiny hypodermic needles, injecting stinging chemicals. The name comes from the Anglo-Saxon *netel,* possibly derived from *noedl* (needle) – after its sharp sting – or *net,* (spin or sew). Widespread in Europe, Asia and the Americas, nettles flourish wherever humans live, enjoying our nitrogen waste, but are also understory plants in wet areas and meadows.

BEST USES AND CULINARY PARTNERS	
COMPLEMENTS	**CULINARY USES**
Salads, pies, soups Puree, pesto, polenta, cheese, butter	Soaking or cooking removes the stinging chemicals Tastes like cucumber or spinach Young (pre-flowering) nettles are great fresh or cooked like spring greens Dried leaves and flowers make herbal tea Nettle beer is a popular UK brew

 ## OILS AND REMEDIES

Nettle shampoos control dandruff, restore colour and make hair glossy.
It is an antidote to hemlock, henbane and nightshade poisoning.
Flogging with nettles was an old remedy for chronic rheumatism.

 ## TRADITIONALLY USED FOR

Bruises and bleeding
Sprains, tendonitis, ague, painful muscles and joints
Arthritis, rheumatism, gout
Urinary and kidney infections, enlarged prostate
Hay fever
Eczema, diabetes, anemia
Stings, venom, insect and mad-dog bites
TB, bronchitis, asthma, flu
Nettlerash, chickenpox
Promoting lactation, skin-toning

 ## DID YOU KNOW?

Fabric, rope and dye can all be made from the plant.
Nettle was invoked in the Anglo-Saxon Nine Herbs charm from the 900s.
Nettle stings may be relieved by many substances including mud and urine.
In Dorset, England there is an annual World Nettle Eating Championship.
Nettles deter bacteria; East European anglers wrapped fish in nettles to preserve their catch.
Nettle leaves in pockets keep you safe from lightning.
Evil is deterred by dry nettle leaves in shoes, under doors and in brooms.
Nettle fodder will feed pigs, fatten fowls, increase egg-production and give horses a sleek coat.
Nettle juice curdles milk; it is a rennet substitute for cheese-making.

DOCK AND SORREL *Rumex*

Named after the Hebrew *rumach* (spear), docks enjoy nitrogen-rich soils and often grow near nettles – thriving well on waste ground, roadsides, ditches, meadows and riversides. Sorrels (including sheep's sorrel, common sorrel and French sorrel) have an acidic taste; some are grown as pot herbs. Originally from the Volga, docks such as monk's rhubarb or herb patience have been cultivated in western Europe since 1573. True rhubarb (*Rheum rhabarbarum*) is from the same family and has been used in Chinese medicine for millennia.

BEST USES AND CULINARY PARTNERS	
COMPLEMENTS	CULINARY USES
Sorrel leaves go with fish, salads, spinach, mashed potatoes Sour docks are served with boiled beef Sorrel and docks complement roast goose or pork	Even the toughest meat, once boiled with docks or sorrels, becomes tender Their acidic leaves make a fine dressing for stewed lamb and veal They can be beaten to a mash with vinegar and sugar to make a tasty green sauce Sorrel can be puréed for *soupe aux herbes* and sauces

 OILS AND REMEDIES

Dock leaves, rubbed over a nettle sting, ease the discomfort. The moist leaf and sap cool the skin and may spread the acid over a larger area, reducing local pain. (Rubbing may also stimulate other nerves to suppress pain signals.)
Dock is an astringent and general blood cleanser.
A tea made from the root may cure boils.
Beating docks into lard makes an ointment.

 TRADITIONALLY USED FOR

Scrofulous disorders, viral infections
Constipation, mild jaundice
Skin diseases; ant and bee stings
Burns, scalds, boils, ulcers, blisters
Scurvy, bleedings, fluxes
Purgatives and laxatives

 DID YOU KNOW?

Broadleaf dock *(Rumex obtusifolius)* was called butter dock because the large leaves were used to wrap butter.
When you slice the root, count the growth rings to date it.
In the fairy story, Hop o' My Thumb hid from a storm under a roadside dock, only to be swallowed by a hungry cow.
Rumex hymenosepalus roots contain up to 25 per cent tannin and are used in leather tanning.

WITCH-HAZEL *Hamamelis*

Witch-hazel has a spicy fragrance and spidery flowers in rich citrus shades of yellow, orange and red that bloom from autumn to spring. *Hamamelis* means 'together with fruit'; its flowers appear at the same time as fruit formed the previous year. Also called winterbloom, spotted alder or snapping hazel, these small trees with silvery grey, cork bark originated in North America, Japan and China and were introduced into Europe by enthusiastic plant hunters.

 ## OILS AND REMEDIES

Witch-hazel produces a volatile oil and its bark contains tannin.

Both leaves and bark are astringent.

Witch-hazel extracts contain antioxidant compounds that may protect against sunburn.

Its tannins help repair broken skin, reduce swelling, and resist bacteria.

Native Americans applied witch-hazel poultices to painful swellings, skin irritations and tumours.

It is generally used externally but a tea made of the leaves or bark eases stomach and bowel complaints.

It should be applied to varicose veins on a moist lint bandage: instant application may even be life-saving.

It removes excess oil from skin, shrinks pores and, used *under* and *around* (bit never *in*) the eyes, reduces discoloration, inflammation and puffiness.

 ## TRADITIONALLY USED FOR

Acne, poison-ivy irritation, shaving rash
Tightening and freshening skin
Preventing spots and pimples
Psoriasis, eczema, cracked or blistered skin
Insect and mosquito bites
Diarrhoea, dysentery, bowel complaints, vomiting
Coughing up blood, TB, cancer
Colds, fevers, reducing inflammation
Hemorrhoids, itching, piles, burns, scalds
Bleeding (nose, stomach, lungs, internal organs)
Bruises, minor burns, ingrown nails
Menorrhagia and abortion after-effects
Post-childbirth soreness
Colitis, teething, pain relief
Drawing tissue together
A tonic and sedative

? DID YOU KNOW?

The common name derives from Middle English *wiche*, meaning pliant or flexible.

Its bendy twigs serve as divining rods.

It is called snapping hazel because its seeds 'explode' to fly about 10 metres (33 feet).

EVENING PRIMROSE *Oenothera*

Also called king's cure-all, sun crop, suncup, sundrop, nightcandle, fever plant, night willowherb, tree primrose and wild beet, *Oenothera* survived successive ice ages to flourish in the Americas. The first to arrive in Europe came from Virginia and reached Padua (Italy) in 1614; now petals glint in most temperate regions, colonizing sand dunes, dry rocky plains, deserts, lakeshores, open woods, hedgerows, roadsides, railway embankments and wastelands. Whether on tiny alpines or three-metre-high species (nearly ten feet), their lemon-yellow, delicately-fragranced blooms open rapidly at dusk and close at sunrise, having by then deepened to gold. Evening bees call by as twilight moths flutter along in the shadows to pollinate it.

BEST USES AND CULINARY PARTNERS	
COMPLEMENTS	CULINARY USES
Both flowers and young roots may garnish salads	Its edible leaves can be cooked like spring greens The roots can also be boiled like potatoes or parsnips Birds like the seeds, too!

 OILS AND REMEDIES

Evening primrose oil helps skin disorders.
It has been marketed as a cancer cure although this is not yet proven.
Its oil contains GLA (linoleic acid) with anti-inflammatory compounds.
It is an astringent and sedative.

 TRADITIONALLY USED FOR

Dry skin conditions
Eczema, psoriasis, acne, rosacea
Rheumatoid arthritis, osteoporosis, muscle strain
Reducing blood pressure
Asthma, whooping cough
Gastro-intestinal disorders
Menstrual cramps, breast tenderness and menopause
Bruises, hemorrhoids, swollen joints
Sore throats, stomachache

 DID YOU KNOW?

It is associated with the Roman moon goddess and huntress, Diana.
Faintly phosphorescent, they make fine moon-garden plants and often decorate moon-ceremony altars.
Bathing in evening primrose tea may enhance beauty and desirability.
Evening primrose brings magic and good luck, especially with hunting.
The Iroquois prescribed it to prevent laziness.
China is the major exporter of its seed.
Its Greek name may mean 'donkey catcher' or 'wine seeker' while the Latin implies 'a plant whose juices may cause sleep'.

BURDOCK *Arctium*

Burdock fruit-burrs entangle hooked spines into the woolly coats of passing sheep (*burra* is Latin for a lock of wool while 'dock' refers to its large, dock-like leaves). *Arctium* derives from *arktos* (Greek for bear) and refers to the fruit's rough, ursine 'hairiness'. Its old English name *herrif* derived from Anglo-Saxon words meaning a hedge that robs or seizes. The plant spread from Northern Europe and Siberia; English and French settlers took it to America in the 1600s.

BEST USES AND CULINARY PARTNERS	
COMPLEMENTS	CULINARY USES
Soft, young leaves can be harvested for salads and go well served with oil and vinegar Burdock once served as a bittering agent in beer	Young roots and tender (pre-flowering) stalks can be boiled; serve sliced, with butter and salt It tastes like artichoke In Japan it is used as a side-dish or appetizer and in soups Try burdock chips instead of potatoes It can be candied with sugar Roots are crisp, sweet and mild Dandelion and burdock cordial was a medieval favourite

 OILS AND REMEDIES

Use dried young roots, or leaves and fruits.
The fruit oil makes a smoothing skin tonic.
Folk remedies say it purifies blood, is antioxidant and prevents disease.
Leaves and stems soothe indigestion.
It was a valuable remedy for stone in the Middle Ages.
Burdock fruits are used in traditional Chinese medicine.

 TRADITIONALLY USED FOR

Eczema, psoriasis, dry scaly skin and scalp
Liver, gall bladder, throat and chest ailments
Boils, scurvy, ulcers, sores
Rheumatism, indigestion, hysteria
Expelling toxic products via urine
Dropsy and kidney afflictions
Snake and mad-dog bites
Reducing blood-sugar and cholesterol levels
Controlling heart rate and blood pressure

 DID YOU KNOW?

It was also called happy major and clot-bur.
The prickly burrs, observed while taking his dog for a walk, were the inspiration for Georges de Mestral's invention of Velcro®.
Most animals avoid eating the burrs but they can cause intestinal hairballs in dogs, lodge in poultry gullets or latch onto bird feathers, preventing flight.
An instrumental piece composed by Christian Wolff in 1970–71 is called *Burdocks*.

MEADOWSWEET *Filipendula ulmaria*

Meadowsweet waves its fernlike foliage and clouds of soft, white, sweetly-perfumed flowers in bogs, ditches, meadows, woodland and beside lakes, ponds and rivers in Europe, eastern USA and Canada. Also called meadsweet, meadow queen, meadow-wort and pride, queen or lady of the meadow, one other name is bridewort, and it was strewn in churches for weddings and made into bridal garlands. In the past it was spread on floors in great dining halls to create a pleasant aroma while keeping fleas and lice at bay, and it was Good Queen Bess's favourite underfoot strew. It can also be added to wine!

BEST USES AND CULINARY PARTNERS	
COMPLEMENTS	CULINARY USES
Beer, wine, Scandinavian mead, vinegars	The flowers add a gentle almond flavour to stewed fruit and jams

 OILS AND REMEDIES

Meadowsweet contains salicylic acid, used to make aspirin, and served the same purposes for centuries.

It is anti-inflammatory, antirheumatic, antibacterial, a diuretic, and good for washing wounds.

A flannel soaked in hot meadowsweet tea makes a soothing compress for arthritis and gout.

A small section of root (peeled, crushed and chewed) soothes headaches.

It helps balance stomach acid.

It was a favourite of medieval herbalists, used by folk healers and monks.

 DID YOU KNOW?

In Welsh mythology, a lovely maiden Blodeuwedd was created by two magicians from meadowsweet and blossom.

Meadowsweet was sacred to druids.

Called *medewurte* (meadwort), after its use in mead, it appears in Geoffrey Chaucer's *The Knight's Tale*.

In Irish mythology, the warlike hero Cú Chulainn bathed in it to calm both his fevers and his rages.

Remnants of flowers or meadowsweet-flavoured mead have been found inside ancient beakers and vessels in Scotland.

It has been found with cremated bodies at a Bronze Age fort in Wales.

 TRADITIONALLY USED FOR

Sunburn, inflamed eyes, swollen joints

Stimulating digestion and bile flow

Liver congestion, cystitis, bladder and kidney infections

Heartburn, hyperacidity, gastritis, peptic ulcers

Diarrhoea, water retention

Common colds; infections, fever

Rheumatism, gout, dropsy

Soothing irritating coughs, wheezing, hoarseness, phlegm

MILK THISTLE *Silybum marianum*

Indigenous to Asia and Europe (especially Mediterranean mountains) and introduced into the Americas by early colonists, milk thistle (Mary, Marian, Our Lady's or Holy thistle) has large, prickly leaves with white veins, purple-red, spiny flowers and dark. mottled fruits – adored by goldfinches. Thriving on dry, rocky soils and wasteland, it is named for its milky sap and has been a medicine for over 2,000 years, used by Ancient Greeks and Romans. In Christian legends, the milk-white leaf veins came from the Virgin Mary's milk, which dropped upon the plant.

BEST USES AND CULINARY PARTNERS	
COMPLEMENTS	CULINARY USES
Salads (use raw, young, de-spined leaves)	The boiled leaves taste as good as spinach Peel the stems of young shoots, soak overnight to remove bitterness, then boil and butter Stems can be baked in pies, tasting like good cabbage Roasted seeds serve as a coffee substitute Roots can be eaten raw, boiled and buttered, or par-boiled and roasted Flowerhead bracts are eaten like globe artichokes

 OILS AND REMEDIES

The seeds, a vital liver medicine, can be life-saving, even for death-cap mushroom poisoning.
In traditional Chinese medicine it relieves toxins, soothes the liver and promotes bile flow.
It helps organs rid toxins after heavy drinking.
It may reduce cell damage after radiation and chemotherapy.
Native Americans used it to treat boils and skin diseases.

 TRADITIONALLY USED FOR

Expelling melancholy and hangovers
Liver disorders, cirrhosis, hepatitis
Jaundice, gallstones, type 2 diabetes
Lowering cholesterol levels
Limiting cancer cells in breast, cervix, prostate
Peritonitis, hemorrhage, varicose veins
Bronchitis, catarrh, pleurisy
Menstrual problems and dropsy
Congestion in liver, spleen, kidneys
Provoking urine flow, to break and expel stones
Toxic chemical exposure and skin disease
Obsessive-compulsive disorder
Milk flow in nursing mothers
Serpent and rabid-dog bites
Ague, plague

 DID YOU KNOW?

The leaves are called pig leaves (pigs like them!)
The Saxons claimed that, if hung upon a man's neck, milk thistle 'setteth snakes to flight'.

VALERIAN *Valeriana officinalis*

Originating in Asia and Europe, valerian (garden heliotrope) thrives in marshy thickets, riversides and by walls. Its plumes of pink, carmine or white flowers are sweetly-scented so attract butterflies *en masse*. Its extracts were used as a perfume in the 1500s and, more recently, in soap manufacture. It was so well regarded in medieval times that it was called All Heal. It attracts cats and rats – it has been suggested that the Pied Piper had valerian roots in his pocket when he led the vermin out of Hamelin.

BEST USES AND CULINARY PARTNERS
CULINARY USES
Anglo-Saxons used it as a salad

 ## OILS AND REMEDIES

The dried root contains a yellowy-brown-green oil.
Root extracts act as a sedative and sleep aid.
The volatile oil is so pungent it has been compared to mature cheese and unwashed feet!
Valerian tea should *not* be made with boiling water; this drives off the lighter oils.
Valerian is cultivated for medical use in England, Prussia, Saxony, Holland and the USA.
It was introduced as an epilepsy treatment by Fabius Calumna in 1592, after he cured himself with it.

 ## TRADITIONALLY USED FOR

Insomnia, cramp, as a diuretic
Stress, anxiety, hysteria, nervous system disorders
Hypochondria, croup
Migraine, neuralgia
Fevers, epilepsy, convulsions
St. Vitus's dance, cholera, plague
Weak eyesight
Cardiac palpitations
Coughs
Bruising

 ## DID YOU KNOW?

Latin *valere* means to be strong and healthy.
During the Middle Ages, people used valerian roots to scent their clothes.
The word *Valerian* occurs in the recipes of eleventh-century Anglo-Saxon medics.
Medieval herbalists called it Capon's Tail.
During World War II it was prescribed to calm nerves during air-raids.
Cats love it; valerian makes people sleepy but is a feline stimulant.

FAIRY TALES

Valerian was placed in Swedish bridegroom outfits, to ward off envy from elves.

 ## WARNING

If taken in excess, it can cause headaches, spasms or hallucinations.

IVY (Common, English or European) *Herdera helix*

Helix (in Greek) means to twist and turn: native to Europe, Africa and Asia, this vigorous, clinging vine sprawls over hedgerows, tree trunks, rocky outcrops and quarries, reaching up to 30 metres (98 feet) high. Slender young shoots are flexible with small, aerial roots and matted pads that cling to rock, bark or bricks; mature shoots are thicker, self-supporting and rootless. Ivy produces its greenish-yellow, nectar-rich flowers only when the branches rise above their support and the leaves become ovate. In winter it shelters wildlife; in spring birds build their nests in it.

BEST USES AND CULINARY PARTNERS
CULINARY USES
During severe winters the bitter berries are beloved by birds like wood pigeons, thrushes and blackbirds, who later disperse the seeds. Ivy is browsed by deer and caterpillars including angle shades, yellow underwing and willow-beauty.

 OILS AND REMEDIES

A drachm of the flowers in wine restrains dysentery.
Culpepper says 'It is an enemy to the nerves and sinews taken *inwardly*, but most excellent *outwardly*.'
Tender twigs boiled in butter and smoothed on the skin ease sunburn.
Water infused with ivy leaves soothes sore, watering eyes.

 TRADITIONALLY USED FOR

Coughs and bronchitis
Breast cancer

 DID YOU KNOW?

Those allergic to ivy leaves usually react to carrots, too.
Growing ivy against a house was thought to keep witches out.
Ancient Greeks thought it prevented drunkenness.
Ivy was dedicated to the Greek god Dionysus (Bacchus) and formed his wreath. Dionysian priestesses carried ivy-entwined staves during sacrificial rites.
Ivy was also the emblem for the Greek muse of comedy, Thalia.
Greek priests presented a wreath of ivy to newly-weds as a fidelity emblem.
An ivy spray on a pole was one of the first inn signs – hence the saying 'Good wine needs no bush'.
Ivy on walls forms a sort of curtain, absorbing rain and moisture and keeping the wall dry.
The Ivy League is a group of eight American colleges and universities – Harvard, Yale, Pennsylvania, Princeton, Columbia, Brown, Dartmouth and Cornell.

 WARNING
Toxic to humans

LIVERWORT *Hepaticae*

Liverwort is a lichen. Its name derives from the Anglo-Saxon *lifer* (liver) and *wyrt* (plant) and it is among the most primitive true plants still in existence. Almost 9,000 species occur from the Arctic to the tropics. Handsome, ribbon-like, with kidney- or heart-shaped leaves and blue (occasionally rose or white) flowers, its soft, veined underside attaches itself to the ground, walls, trees or molehills. A few species are submerged aquatics but most thrive on damp soil or rotting logs, along shaded banks or on rocks by streams. Many especially enjoy shady tropical areas. Early herbalists thought that *Marchantia* liverwort had liver-like lobes and, under the Doctrine of Signatures, it was often used to treat liver ailments.

 OILS AND REMEDIES

Leaves and flowers serve as a diuretic, astringent and a soothing film over slow-healing injuries.

It is a general liver tonic.

It has been used to stimulate appetite, metabolism, pancreas and blood circulation.

Liverwort increases heart blood supply and regulates bowel function.

Distilled in water, it is used for freckles and sunburn.

Bruised and boiled in beer, it was used to 'cool the heat' of both liver and kidneys.

 TRADITIONALLY USED FOR

Dog bites and hydrophobia
Liver problems and over-indulgence
Stomach pains, indigestion, gallstones
High cholesterol, yellow jaundice
Varicose veins, hernia, hemorrhoids
Nerves, menopausal symptoms
Urinary passage and skin diseases
Coughs, chest diseases, consumption
Running sores and scabs
Inflammation, ringworm

 DID YOU KNOW?

The English word *wort* means 'a small plant'.

Liverworts are often pricked with little red parasites.

Hepatica (also used to treat liver diseases) is sometimes referred to as liverwort but this is incorrect.

Ancient liverwort fossils show the earliest evidence of plants colonizing the land in Argentinian rocks dating from 473 million years ago.

Popular in aquariums, liverwort branches float on the surface, providing a good habitat for small invertebrates and fish.

 WARNING

Poisonous in large doses to humans, pigs, sheep, horses, cattle.

LUNGWORT *Pulmonaria*

Thriving on the edges of deciduous woodland and under trees, especially oaks and beeches in Europe and western Asia, lungwort has broad, strikingly-patterned green, grey and silver-splashed leaves. These are wavy edged, arranged in rosettes, and may be spotted black, blue or pale green. The oval leaf shape does resemble a lung – hence the name. Pink, funnel-shaped buds mutate into lilac and then bright blue jewel-like flowers, the variation in colours often occurring simultaneously as spring arrives. An early source of nectar and pollen, they attract bees, butterflies and humming birds.

 ## ITS NAMES INCLUDE

Adam and Eve
Bedlam cowslip
Beggar's basket
Bethlehem sage
Bugloss cowslip
Common lungwort
Jerusalem sage
Jerusalem cowslip
Lady's cowslip
Lady's milk
Mary's honeysuckle
Mary's tears
Oak lungs
Sage of Bethlehem
Soldiers and sailors
Spotted dog
Virgin Mary's honeysuckle

 ## OILS AND REMEDIES

It is a mild diuretic.
Used since medieval times to cure lung problems, modern research has discovered that it is indeed a useful remedy.
A leaf infusion soothes coughs and catarrh.
It serves in lotions 'to stay the moist humours that flow to ulcers, and hinder their healing, as also to wash all other ulcers in the privy parts of a man or woman'.

 ## TRADITIONALLY USED FOR

Respiratory problems, lung complaints, asthma, coughs, wheezing, shortness of breath
Flu, colds, catarrh, hoarseness
Tuberculosis
Inflammation
Diarrhea, hemorrhoids
Wounds, ulcers, sores
Excessive menstrual flow

 ## DID YOU KNOW?

The lungwort sold as a drug today is sometimes a moss known as oak lungs and lung moss.
Since its speckled leaves resemble lungs its use was partly founded on the Doctrine of Signatures.
Its nickname 'Soldiers and Sailors' relates to how the changing colours of the flowers recall the red uniforms of the British Army and the blue ones of the Navy.
This is one of the few plants that will grow under toxic black walnut trees.

WOLFSBANE *Aconitum*

Known as monkshood, leopard's bane, devil's helmet, friar's cap or blue rocket, this was an early medicinal perennial – grown since medieval times and long known for its powerful magic (described by Severus Snape during Harry Potter's first Potions class). Originally from mountainous regions, rocky glens and high meadows (especially the Swiss Alps and North Tyrol), its toxins have been used to kill wolves, ibex, bears, tigers and whales. Blue, purple, white, yellow or pink flowers are helmet or hood-shaped (thus monkshood) and beloved by butterflies and bumblebees. Its active poison is most formidable.

 ## OILS AND REMEDIES

The extract is made from leaves and flowering tops.
Aconite is a most useful drug, popular in homoeopathy.
It lessens pulse rate in early stages of fever.
Greek, Roman, traditional Chinese and Hindu medicine describe aconite.

 ## DID YOU KNOW?

The root juice was used to poison arrow tips for warfare and wolf hunting.
In some countries, it is illegal to cultivate wolfsbane without a permit.
It is said to work against vampires (including Count Dracula) and werewolves.
In 2009 the so-called 'Curry Killer', Lakhvir Singh, murdered her lover with a curry dish laced with aconite.

 ## POISONS AND TOXINS

Symptoms include burning, tingling, numb tongue and mouth, vomiting, a sensation of crawling ants on the skin, laboured breathing, irregular weak pulse, cold clammy skin, giddiness, staggering, sweating, headache, confusion – followed by severe pain, convulsions, paralysis, seizures and heart failure.
Toxin exists in all parts but especially the root.
The only post-mortem signs are of asphyxia.
The root's resemblance to horseradish has caused fatalities.
It will kill a sparrow in seconds.
Aconite may be the poison Medea prepared for the Greek hero Theseus.
It is used in witches' flying ointments.
In the East Indies, *A. ferox* has been used for poisoning wells, spears, darts and arrows.
Even hungry field mice leave this plant well alone.

 ## TRADITIONALLY USED FOR

WARNING: Poisonous plant: do not try these at home
Neuralgia, lumbago
Rheumatism, arthritis
Cardiac failure, shock, hypothermia
Tonsillitis, laryngitis, headaches
Pneumonia, pleurisy, bronchitis, croup, coughs
Diarrhoea, impotence
Grief, fear, anger, suicidal tendencies
Eye and ear infections
Measles
Scorpion stings, bruises

 ## WARNING
Severely toxic.

DEADLY NIGHTSHADE *Atropa belladonna*

Atropos was one of three Ancient Greek Fates, who wove and cut the threads of life and death; *belladonna* (beautiful lady) was inspired by Italian beauties who dilated their pupils with nightshade eyedrops – adding to their allure but risking blindness. Described by the Ancients and herbal authors from the 1500s, the purple, bell-shaped flowers dangled merrily in Europe, Asia and Algeria, and today grace wastelands, quarries and woodlands in North America as well. The cherry-sized black berries ooze an inky, intensely sweet juice that children enjoy to their cost – with fatal results. It has also served as an instrument of torture, a narcotic and a favourite poison of assassins.

 ## OILS AND REMEDIES

It served as a surgery anesthetic prior to the Middle Ages.
Scarcely any eye operation is performed without using it to dilate pupils.
It increases heart rate by 20 to 40 beats per minute, without diminishing its force.
During surgery it is applied to the cardiac region to allay palpitations, pain and distress.
A poultice of belladonnna leaves was once held to be a cancer cure.
Called Twilight Sleep, it was used to alleviate childbirth.

 ## TRADITIONALLY USED FOR

An opium and chloroform antidote
A painkiller, anti-irritant and sleeping agent
An antispasmodic in intestinal colic and asthma
Sore throats, whooping cough
Pneumonia collapse, typhoid, scarlet fever
Neuralgia, gout, rheumatism, sciatica
Injuries, sprains, corns, bunions
Diarrhoea, irritable bowel syndrome
Parkinson's disease
Motion sickness
Poisoning arrow tips

 ## DID YOU KNOW?

By taking tiny sips, an assassin builds up sufficient resistance to be able to drink a little and suggest it is safe, encouraging the victim to swallow the sweet, fatal poison.
Belladonna was thought to belong to the devil, who trims and tends it.
Witches used it as an ointment to help them take to the air (or at least think they were flying).
It was used to poison enemy troops by the Ancient Romans, by Scotland's Macbeth, and by Scotland's King Duncan I. In 1020 he gave a nightshade drink to Danish invaders, killing them without a battle.
The mandrake root (a nightshade relative) resembles a human body and was believed to contain a spirit that brought great fortune but which emitted an unholy shriek when tugged from the earth.
The sleeping potion in Romeo and Juliet may have contained nightshade or mandrake.

 WARNING
Severely toxic.

FASCINATING FACTS

LOVE AND MARRIAGE

Aphrodisiac herbs and spices include dill, rocket, garlic, ginger, ginkgo biloba, ginseng, horny goat weed, maca root, nutmeg, oat seed, saffron and summer savoury.

Herbalists describe **water lily stems** as an anaphrodisiac – it *reduces* sexual cravings.

Basil is precious to lovers in Italy where young men wore a sprig of basil to indicate their intended marriage.

Borage
This was sometimes smuggled into the drink of a prospective husband to give him sufficient courage to propose.

Marigolds, marjoram and thyme
On St. Luke's Day, take marigold flowers, sprigs of marjoram and thyme, and a little wormwood; dry them, rub to a powder, sift through fine lawn. Simmer over a fire,

Marigold

adding virgin honey and vinegar. Anoint yourself with this when you go to bed, saying the following thrice:
St. Luke, St. Luke, be kind to me,
In dreams let me my true love see …
And you will dream of your future partner.

Marjoram and **Myrtle** have both been traditionally used in wedding garlands and bouquets.

Peas
If a girl desires to determine who she will marry, let her seek a green peascod in which are full nine peas, and write on a piece of paper:
Come in, my dear,
And do not fear.
She must enclose this paper in the peascod and lay it under the door. The first person who comes into the room will become her husband.

Basil

Rosemary

In the 1500s, bridesmaids gave rosemary sprigs to the groom while the bride wore it to remember her family. Rosemary was

Rosemary

added to the wine that toasted the couple to make the good wishes come true.

A rosemary branch, gilded and tied with silk ribbons, was presented to wedding guests as a symbol of love and loyalty.

If one young person tapped another with a rosemary sprig with an open flower, it was said they would fall in love.

If a few potted plants were given a suitor's name; whichever grew best represented one's sweetheart.

If rosemary grew abundantly, the woman ruled the roost; so much so that in the 1500s, men sometimes dug up strong bushes to prove they were in charge.

A man indifferent to the scent of rosemary was said to be incapable of true love.

MAGIC AND WITCHCRAFT

Centaury was said to being powerful against *wykked sperytis*.

Deadly nightshade and henbane were both powerful ingredients in medicines and were part of a witch's 'portfolio'.

Dill and **Garlic** both keep witches and evil away; in the Middle Ages, dill was hung above doorways.

Flax

In the Middle Ages flax flowers were believed to offer protection against sorcery.

Flax

The Bohemians have a belief that if seven-year-old children dance among flax, they will become beautiful.

Foxglove and **cowslip** blossoms have mottled spots; like the spots on butterfly wings and peacocks or pheasants, these were said to mark where the elves had placed their fingers.

Honeysuckle bowers were often grown around doors and in gardens to ward off witches and evil spirits. If placed under a pillow, honeysuckle invoked pleasant dreams.

Ivy
Growing ivy against the side of a house was thought to keep witches away.

Nettle
People would put nettles into their pockets to be safe from lightning.

Dry leaves popped into shoes meant that evil powers couldn't lead you into dangerous places.

Nettles under the door stopped evil coming *in*.

A nettle broom would sweep evil *from* the room.

The most potent magic is in mature (but not old) nettles, gathered by the light of a young moon, ideally on a Tuesday.

Never pull up the whole plant, roots and all

Primrose

– if the nettles lose contact with the land, their power diminishes.

Primroses
To deter witches leave a primrose on the doorstep on May Day Eve and, on May Day, hang primrose balls on cows' tails.

Bunches of primroses in cowsheds stop fairies stealing milk.

It is lucky to bring thirteen primroses indoors but unlucky to bring in one alone.

If you let primroses die, the fairies will be upset.

Rosemary
A sprig outside the home repels witches.

St. John's Wort, fennel and violets
defended against witchcraft and wicked spirits.

Speedwell repels witches, demons, devils and other assorted bogeymen.

WITCH OINTMENTS

Supplied by the devil or an experienced witch, herbal mixes of deadly nightshade (belladonna), opium poppy, monkshood, wolfsbane, henbane and hemlock were used to anoint a broomstick or chair to enable it to fly through the air or dance at the Witches' Sabbath. Small doses of belladonna and other alkaloids could, indeed, induce a dream-like state, hallucinations – and sometimes the sensation of being airborne (possibly broomstick-flying) – due to its stimulation of the central nervous system.

In *The book of all forbidden arts,* published in 1456, Johannes Hartlieb said that demons made a salve from seven herbs mixed with bird blood and animal lard. It was rubbed on benches, chairs, rakes or oven forks to make them fly.

Deadly nightshade

MUSIC AND ART

Parsley, sage, rosemary and thyme feature in the folk song *Scarborough Fair.*

In the 1980s and early '90s, New Zealand reggae band Herbs had ten Top 20 singles hits.

Austrian composer Ernst Toch (1887–1964) wrote a *Cantata of the Bitter Herbs.*

In 2015 an advertisement by the food company Schwartz featured several herbs and spices exploding in time to a piece of music.

Some herb growers believe that playing classical music near herbs helps them to thrive.

Hildegard von Bingen, a 12th-century composer of music, catalogued the medicinal effects of over 200 herbs.

Rosemary and Thyme is a television thriller series.

The iris has been painted by Leonardo da Vinci, Durer, Renoir, Cezanne, Gauguin, Monet and Van Gogh.

A series of some 250 oil paintings by French

Impressionist Claude Monet (1840–1926) featured water lilies (otherwise used to stop diarrhoea!)

In Boccaccio's 14th-century book *Decameron*, Lisabetta places the decapitated head of her dead lover in a pot of basil, which she waters with her tears, inspiring a poem by John Keats and a painting by John Everett Millais.

HERB SPECIFICS

Anise: Romans paid taxes with anise, and it was used in cough drops.

Borage

Belladonna (deadly nightshade) is supposed to have been the plant used by the Parthians to poison the Roman legionnaires of Mark Antony during the Parthian Wars.

Early anesthesia initially used plant sources such as poppies and belladonna, then drugs like morphine and scopolamine to induce what was termed a Twilight Sleep during surgery or childbirth.

Macbeth of Scotland used belladonna to poison the troops of the invading King Harold of England.

Borage

The Romans believed this to be an antidepressant; ancient Celtic warriors took it for courage.

Calendula

In Holland, the dried flowers flavoured broths and potions. Grocers or Spicesellers kept barrels filled with them.

Chervil was said to warm old, cold stomachs; eating a whole plant would cure hiccups.

Chives

Bunches hung in your home were used to drive away diseases and evil.

Dill

The Romans made wreaths and garlands out of dill – as a sign of wealth and status.

In Ancient Greece athletes massaged dill essence over their bodies, as a muscle toner.

Soldiers used burnt dill seeds to help wounds heal faster.

Hippocrates had a recipe for a dill mouthwash.

Evening primrose

Some claim that this magical herb might be good for shape-shifting.

Associated with the moon goddess and huntress Diana, it brings good luck to hunters.

This is a popular fairy plant, from which fairies collect dew to make potions.

Chamomile

Egyptians believed this was a sacred gift and offered its flowers to the Sun God.

Chamomile was used in ancient Egyptian mummification.

Chamomile has been traditionally used to treat more than 100 medical conditions.

Anglo-Saxons named it as one of the Nine Sacred Herbs.

Called the Plant's Physician and vaunted in old herbals, chamomile works well as an emollient with anti-inflammatory effects.

Fennel

Bunches of fennel were used to drive off witches. It was also used in love potions.

Garlic was thought to give strength and courage – and to resist evil powers.

The ancient Greek philosopher-scientist Aristotle noted garlic's use against the fear of water.

Goldenrod

In 1788 a 10-year-old, after taking a goldenrod infusion for some months, passed 15 large stones and 50 over the size of a pea.

Babies washed in baths with goldenrod leaves grow up happy with a great sense of humour.

Chamomile

Frequent handling of goldenrod can cause allergic reactions so florists generally avoid it.

Iris orris root

In ancient Greece and Rome the Iris orris root was used in perfume and unguents to soften skin. The heavy, earthy-smelling resinous roots develop a violet odour as they dry, continually intensifying.

Native Americans (and colonial settlers) used it to treat wounds, earache, ulcers and cholera.

The 1480 Wardrobe accounts of England's king Edward IV tell how, mixed with anise, it was used as a linen perfume – and it was probably the 'swete clothe' celebrated in Elizabethan times.

Ivy has always been a plant of superstition… If ivy stays fresh in a bowl of water from New Year's Eve until Twelfth Night, this means happiness ahead … but if black spots appear near the leaf bases, this suggests foot difficulties; marks near the stem presage head problems.

A handful of bruised ivy gently boiled in wine removes its intoxicating effects.

Binding the brow with ivy leaves was said to prevent intoxication.

Because of its pagan associations, ivy Christmas decorations were banned by the early Christian Church.

Before he discovered the grape vine, the ancient Greek god Dionysos was said to have eaten ivy berries to induce intoxication.

Lavender is one of the oldest perfumes.

In Ancient Roman times, a pound of lavender flowers cost a month's wages.

In medieval times, powdered lavender was used as a condiment.

In the 1970s, a new *herbes de Provence* included lavender.

Ladies of the manor used lavender to scent linen stores.

It was sewn into sweet bags, used as an air freshener and mixed with beeswax to make furniture polish. Traditionally, it was planted by the laundry room so that bedlinen and clothing could be stretched across the plants to dry while absorbing the scent.

It also repelled insects.

England's Queen Elizabeth I used lavender as a perfume and drank it in tea to soothe her migraines.

Marshmallow

Boiling the root makes a thick syrup glue.

Mallow was once used to decorate friends' graves.

The bark can be a hemp substitute.

Followers of the ancient Greek philosopher Pythagoras considered mallows sacred, as the flowers always turned towards the sun.

Mint was believed to cure hiccups and counteract sea-serpent stings.

The Romans wore peppermint wreaths on their heads.

Ancient Romans and Greeks used mint to flavour cordials as well as adding it to their bathwater.

Mint comes in more than 30 varieties.

Myrtle

In the Roman epic *The Aeneid* the spears that impaled the young Trojan prince Polydorus transformed into myrtle, marking his grave.

The Myrtles Plantation, Louisiana, is said to be one of America's most haunted sites.

In neo-pagan rituals, myrtle is sacred to May Day.

Myrtle was sacred to goddesses Aphrodite (Venus) and Demeter, and was held by one of the Graces.

Myrtle

Nettle

You should pick nettles on a Tuesday… but never by the light of a young moon.

Don't uproot the whole plant or the nettles lose their power.

The figure of speech 'to grasp the nettle' probably originated from Aesop's fable *The Boy and the Nettle*.

If a nettle plant is grasped firmly rather than brushed against, it does not sting so fiercely; the hairs are crushed flat and less able to penetrate the skin.

The Hungarian saying, 'No lightning strikes the nettle' means 'bad things never happen to bad people'.

In Germany, to 'sit in nettles' means to get into trouble.

Dispel a fever by uprooting a nettle, then reciting the names of the patient and their parents.

Nettle extracts are used by bodybuilders to increase free testosterone.

If planted near beehives, nettles drive away

frogs.

Russian country folk stained eggs yellow with nettle juice on Maundy Thursday.

Rubbing nettle juice into a leaky wooden tub renders its seams watertight.

Nettles have been used to make cloth since the Bronze Age, especially in Russia, Scandinavia, Poland and Germany. In 1915, 1.3 million kilograms of nettles (for uniforms and fabric) were collected in Germany.

Urine relieves nettle stings.

Applying stinging nettles to the skin relieves rheumatism and eczema.

However, a sting from some Indian nettle species 'scorches' the skin for up to a year and may cause symptoms akin to tetanus.

Oregano is used for 'sour humours' that plagued old farmers. It is also an antidote

for scorpion and spider bites.

Parsley

It is unlucky to transplant parsley, especially from an old garden into a new one.

In ancient Greece, parsley was planted on graves; *'to be in need of parsley'* meant death was imminent.

The Greeks also used parsley for funeral wreaths and in garlands for winning athletes.

Early immigrants to the Americas took parsley with them.

'It is very important not to mistake hemlock for parsley.' – French encyclopedist Denis Diderot (1713–84) was here referring to cow parsley, not the culinary variety!

Parsley is said to repel head lice and attract rabbits.

Poppies

British Legion poppies were designed to be made by someone with only one hand.

In Greek and Roman mythology, poppies were offered to the dead.

Othello is the only play by William Shakespeare that refers to poppies.

Poppy was the 13th most popular name for a baby girl in England and Wales in 2012.

Rosemary

'I let it run all over my garden walls, not only because my bees love it but because it is the herb sacred to remembrance and to friendship.' – Sir Thomas More (1478–

Poppies

1535).
Rosemary in your hair will improve your
    memory.
A sprig under your pillow will protect you from
    evil spirits.

Sage was said to ward off bubonic plague or
    Black Death.
As a grief-alleviator, sage was often planted in
    graveyards.
Hungry toads love chomping young sage
    plants but rue will repel them.
Aztecs often paid their tributes and taxes in
    highly prized sage seeds.

A medieval treatise claims, 'The desire of sage
    is to render man immortal.'

Tarragon
Put this in your shoes before long walking
    trips to give strength.
It has been used to relieve toothache.

Thyme was spread by the Romans as they
    conquered Europe; they needed it for their
    bee-keeping and honey production.
Burning thyme gets rid of insects in your house.
A bed of thyme was thought to be a home for
    fairies.

Thyme

Many ladies embroidered a spray of thyme on tokens they presented to their chivalrous knights.

Thyme is often used in cough drops.

Violets

Some butterflies feed entirely on violets.

Flowers and leaves are collected separately for making perfume, confectionary and syrup.

In the 20th century Egypt became a major producer of violet leaf *absolue*.

French emperor Napoleon Bonaparte (1769–1821), known as Corporal Violet, covered his beloved Josephine's grave with violets. He wore a locket containing violets plucked from her grave. When he left for exile on the isle of Elba he promised to return in the violet season. Enquiring 'Do you like violets?' became a secret code of his supporters, and the violet was adopted as the emblem of the Imperial Napoleonic party.

Water lily

Yellow pond lily rootstock, crushed and boiled in milk, will eliminate cockroaches and beetles.

The smoke of the yellow pond lily repels crickets.

POWERFUL HERBS: CANCER TREATMENTS

Statistics indicate that fifty years ago only one in 3,000 people were known to get cancer. Thirty years ago, one in five were diagnosed as having the disease. Today the figures have increased to one in three. Inevitably, a rising number of patients and their relatives seek the means to recovery, especially from the most life-threatening forms of cancer.

Back in the 1800s, Edward Bach was offering preparations in which tiny amounts of plant material were diluted in a mixture of water and brandy. Cancer Research UK advises that although flower remedies such as these are sometimes promoted as being capable of boosting the immune system, 'there is no scientific evidence to prove that flower remedies can control, cure or prevent any type of disease, including cancer.'

Obviously, no alternative treatment should ever be considered without consulting a medical practitioner and after ensuring that there are no conflicts with any on-going medication. Only the advice of trained and recommended medical herbalists should be sought and it should be noted that, as with conventional medication, some herbs do have side-effects. There is no 'official' support for botanical treatments. Indeed, Cancer Research UK says that there is currently no strong evidence that herbal remedies can treat, prevent or cure cancer. And, similarly in the USA, the American Cancer Society notes that there is no reliable evidence for herbal cures and it does not support such remedies.

Sadly, there are all too many ineffective cures on offer and, moreover, a growing number of companies seeking to accrue profits through promoting these. Nonetheless, the ancient history of herbal remedies and their more recent counterparts is not to be totally overlooked and, indeed, is what this book is all about! Although the book can in no way offer an opinion or recommend any herbal treatment, it provides an interesting update on the historical data. Here is what *today's* herbalists, despite the official viewpoints, believe particular herbs can do to help treat cancer.

Astragalus *(Huang Qi):* This Chinese herb is an immune system booster, said to stimulate the body's natural production of interferon and to help the immune system identify rogue cells.

Berberis *(Podophyllum peltanum):* This slow-acting purgative is believed to be pro-active, especially against ovarian cancer.

Bloodroot *(Sanguinaria canadensis):* It is claimed that this can help to shrink cancer tumours and sarcomas.

Butcher's broom *(Ruscus aculeatus):* Active ruscogenins are said to shrink tumours and have anti-oestrogenic abilities, hence its use in breast cancer treatment.

Cat's claw *(Uncaria tormentosa):* A powerful immuno-stimulant, it is believed to enhance white cell action and reduce tumour size, particularly skin cancers. It also helps reduce the side-effects of chemo- and radiotherapy.

Chaparral *(Larrea mexicana):* This appears to boost the immune system, stop metastases and reduce tumour size, especially breast cancers. It is also an antioxidant and anti-microbial, with low toxicity.

Curcumin: This spice *(Curcuma longa* or turmeric root) has been shown to have significant anti-microbial and anti-inflammatory effects and it is useful for treating polyps and colon cancer. New research indicates the shrinking of cancer tumours and inhibited blood supply growth

Bloodroot

to tumours. It is a powerful antioxidant with liver protection benefits.

Dang Shen root *(Codonopsis pilosula):* This root increases both white and red blood cell levels, so can help patients undergoing chemotherapy and radiotherapy.

Echinacea: This immune-system booster is used when treating brain tumours and may increase the levels of certain immune white cells.

Feverfew: This herb can help to kill leukaemia cells and the US Food and Drug Agency has put the active ingredient, parthenolide, on its fast-track programme for expedited review.

Ginger This has been promoted as a cancer treatment that may halt tumour growth; however, according to the American Cancer Society, the available scientific evidence does not yet support this.

Goldenseal: Goldenseal is generally anti-microbial and is used to deter parasites. Research in America indicates that leukaemia patients who took this had reduced liver toxicity and chemotherapy side-effects. There is some evidence that it has its own anti-cancer effects too.

Juice therapy: Some sources claim that juice made from raw fruit and vegetables may help to slow aging and cancer growth; however the American Cancer Society says, 'There is no convincing scientific evidence that extracted juices are healthier than whole foods.'

Mistletoe

Wormwood

Mangosteen: This fruit, native to Southeast Asia, is promoted for treating a variety of ailments, including cancer.

Mistletoe: This parasitic plant was proposed as a cancer cure by mystic Rudolf Steiner (1861–1925), who believed it needed to be harvested when the planetary alignment most influenced its potency. As yet however, his claim has remained unsupported by clinical trials.

Mushrooms: These are often promoted as useful for cancer treatment but there is currently no official evidence to lend these claims credence.

Pau D'Arco: This tree bark is strongly anti-bacterial, anti-yeast and antimicrobial. New research indicates that its active ingredients (quinoids) possess immune-strengthening abilities and it seems to help in cases of blood and lymph cancers.

Red clover (Herb of Hippocrates): This has the anti-oestrogen ingredient genistein. Research from various centres including the Royal Marsden Hospital, London, has shown its potential in treatment against oestrogen-driven cancers, from breast to prostate.

Sheep sorrel: This cleanser aids healthy tissue regeneration and may help 'normalize' damaged cells and tissue.

Skullcap (Scutellaria barbata): Research has indicated action against cancers of the lung, stomach and intestines.

Sutherlandia (Cancer bush): Peer-reviewed research studies indicate that this herb is anti-inflammatory, antiviral and antifungal. It boosts the immune system and inhibits tumour necrosis in cancer patients.

Thorowax (Hare's ear – *Bulpleurum scorzoneraefolium*): Research has shown this can enhance the production of natural interferon and it seems especially useful in bone cancer.

Venus flytrap: An extract from this carnivorous plant is promoted as a treatment for a variety of human ailments including skin cancer, a claim as yet unsupported by official scientific evidence.

Violets: The British Pharmacopoeia states that 'Violet leaves have been used with benefit to allay the pain in cancerous growths, especially in the throat, which no other treatment relieved, and several reputed cures have been recorded.'

Walnuts (*Juglans*): Black walnut seeds have been promoted as able to remove parasites from the intestinal tract and thus to aid cancer cures – as yet unproven.

Wheatgrass: The chlorophyll in freshly juiced wheatgrass acts as a blood purifier and cleanses the liver and kidneys, improving circulation while improving blood and tissue oxygen levels. Oxygen is said to be the cancer cell's enemy.

Wormwood: This herb is used as an anti-microbial, anti-yeast and anti-malarial drug and to relieve the yeast excess that may form during treatments for certain cancers such as leukaemia. Some experts think that excess yeast may even trigger certain cancers.

Chinese Milk Vetch

Venus Flytrap

HERBS ACROSS THE WORLD
National Herbs, State Symbols and Popular Herbs

BANGLADESH: Water Lily *(Nymehaea nouchali)*
BELARUS: Common flax *(Linum usitatissimum)*
BELGIUM: Red Poppy *(Papaver rhoeas)*
BERMUDA: Blue-eyed Grass *(Sisyrinchium montanum)*
BHUTAN: Blue poppy *(Meconopsis betonicifolia)*
BOHEMIA: Thyme *(Thymus vulgaris)*

Thyme

CANADA
Basil is the most popular herb in Canada, followed by dill, rosemary, mint, thyme, chives and oregano. 4,000 medicinal herbs grow naturally or under cultivation here. Their use has been documented elsewhere for over 2,000 years. Canada's first Annual Herb and Spice Conference was held in Guelph, Ontario in 2004.
    NEW BRUNSWICK: Purple violet *(Viola)*
    NUNAVUT: Purple saxifrage *(Saxifraga oppositifolia)*
    QUEBEC: Blue Flag Iris *(Iris versicolor)*
    YUKON: Fireweed *(Chamerion angustifolium)*
CROATIA: Iris Croatica *(Hrvatska perunika)*
CUBA: Ginger Lily *(Hedychium)*
DENMARK: Red clover *(Trifolium pratense)* and English Holly *(Ilex aquifolium)*
ENGLAND: The first week of May is National Herb Week
EGYPT: Lotus or water lily *(Nymphea)*
FRANCE: Iris *(Iris)*
    TOULOUSE: The violet *(Viola)*: in 1323 the Floral Games conferred a golden violet for the best minds of the time – and still do today
GREECE: Bear's Breech *(Acanthus mollis)*
    ATHENS: The ancient Greeks made the violet *(Viola)* the official Athens symbol

Basil

Hibiscus

GREENLAND: Willow Herb *(Epilobium)*

GUYANA: Water lily *(Victoria regia)*

HUNGARY: Paprika *(capsicum annuum)*, onion *(Allium cepa)* and garlic *(Allium sativum)* are firm favourites here

HAITI: Hibiscus *(Hibiscus)*

IRELAND: Shamrock or Cloverleaf *(Trifolium pratense)*

INDONESIA: Arabian jasmine *(Jasminum sambacis* or 'melati putih')

JORDAN: Black Iris *(Iris nigricans)*

LATVIA: Ox-eye Daisy *(Leucanthemum vulgare)* or Pipene *(Leucanthemum vulgare)*

LIBERIA: Pepper

MALAYSIA: Hibiscus *(Hibiscus)*

LITHUANIA: Rue or Herb of Grace *(Ruta graveolens)*

MALAYSIA: Hibiscus *(Hibiscus rosa-sinensis)*

MALTA: Maltese Centaury *(Paleocyanus Crasifoleus)* and Hibiscus *(Hibiscus)*

MOLOSSIA REPUBLIC: Common Sagebrush *(Artemisia tridentata)*

Jasmine *(left: Shamrock)*

NETHERLANDS: Marigold *(Calendula officinalis)*

NORWAY: Heather *(Calluna vulgaris)*

PARAGUAY: Jasmine-of-the-Paraguay *(Jasminum)*

PERU: Kantuta, the Inca magic flower *(Cantua buxifolia)*

PHILIPPINES: Sampagita jasmine *(Jasminum sambac)*

POLAND: Corn Poppy *(Papaver rhoeas)*

PORTUGAL: Lavender *(Lavandula)*

PUERTO RICA: Puerto Rican hibiscus, or Flor de Maga *(Montezuma speciossisima)*

RUSSIA: Chamomile *(Matricaria recutita)*

SCOTLAND: Cotton thistle *(Onopordum acanthium)*

SOUTH KOREA: Rose of Sharon *(Hibiscus syriacus)*

SWEDEN: Twinflower *(Linnea borealis)*

SWITZERLAND: Edelweiss *(Leontopodium alpinum)*

USA

DELAWARE: Sweet goldenrod *(Solidago odora)* is the state herb

HAWAII: Hibiscus *(Hibiscus)* is the state flower

ILLINOIS: Violet *(Viola)*

KENTUCKY: Goldenrod *(Solidago)*

MAINE: Wintergreen *(Gaultheria procumbens)*

NEBRASKA: Goldenrod *(Solidago)*

SOUTH CAROLINA: Goldenrod *(Solidago)*

WASHINGTON STATE: Western Hemlock *(Tsuga heterophylla)*

WYOMING: Indian paintbrush *(Castilleja)*

From the late 1800s GAHANNA city, a suburb of Columbus, Ohio, has been called 'The Herb Capital of Ohio', a name made official in 1972.

WALES: Leek *(Allium)*

Thistle

Alium

SENSE AND EMOTIONS

The Language of Herbs and Flowers

Plants, particularly flowering plants, have been associated with special meanings for thousands of years – throughout Europe, Asia and the Middle East. They were used as symbols in the Bible, given emblematic attributes by William Shakespeare, and became an obsession in the Turkish Ottoman Court, from whence the notion spread through Europe, to be encapsulated in the 1800s in France, Victorian England and the United States. Gifts of blooms, plants, buttonholes, posies and bouquets became a means to send coded messages to one's beloved or prospective sweetheart at a time when sexual stirrings were taboo and even piano legs were covered to avoid offence.

The language of flowers, a charming way to convey emotions, includes:

allium – unity, humility, patience
aloe – grief, affection
angelica – inspiration
balm – sympathy
balsam – impatience, touch-me-not
basil – hatred, sweet, good or best
bay leaf – I change but in death
bergamot (wild bergamot or bee balm) –
   compassion, sweet virtues

betony – surprise, healing
borage – bluntness, your intentions embarrass
   me
burdock (importunity/touch me not)
calendula – sacred affections, joy, remembrance,
   grief
catnip (catmint) – intoxification with love
celandine (great and little) – joys to come
centaury – felicity

Chamomile.
Facing page: clover.

chamomile – patience and energy in adversity

chicory – frugality

chives – why do you weep?

cinquefoil – maternal affection

clover – be mine, think of me, industry

cowslip – pensiveness, happiness

cress – stability

dandelion – faithfulness, happiness

dill – good spirits, lust

dock – patience

dragon root – ardour

elder – zealousness

fennel – worthy of praise or flattery

feverfew – fire, warmth, protection, you light up my life

flax – fate, domestic industry, feeling your kindness

foxglove – insincerity, stateliness, youth

garlic – courage, charm against evil, I can't stand you, strength of character

gentian – sweet be thy dreams, intrinsic worth, integrity

geranium – present preference

germander speedwell – facility

gloxinia – proud spirit

goldenrod – allow me time to decide

henbane – for males to attract love from females

herb Robert – steadfastness, I am yours, come what may

Dandelion.
Facing page: Thyme, rosemary.

honeysuckle – love, 'With this I pledge my love'

horehound – good health

hyssop – cleanliness

ivy – friendship, matrimony, fidelity, constancy

iris (flag) – messages

iris (German) – flame

juniper – succour, protection

kingcup (marsh marigold) – desiring riches

lavender – acknowledgment, suspicion and distrust, devotion, loyalty

lemon balm – sympathy, don't misuse me

liverwort – confidence

lovage – hidden virtues, cleanliness

lungwort – thou art my life

mallow – mildness

marigold – despair, grief, honesty

marjoram – blushes

marsh mallow – beneficence

meadowsweet – uselessness

mint – grief, homeliness, wisdom, eternal refreshment, virtue

mugwort – happiness and travel, be not weary

morning glory (ipomoea) – affectation

myrtle – marriage and love

nasturtium – optimism, splendour, patriotism

nettle – cruel, slander

nightshade – truth

orchid – delicate beauty

oregano – joy and happiness

ox-eye daisy – a token

parsley – useful knowledge, festivity, joy, victory, the woman of the house is boss

Mint. Facing page: Nasturtium.

pennyroyal – flee away

peppermint – cordiality, warmth of feeling

pheasant's eye – remembrance

pimpernel – change, assignation

poppy – consolation, extravagance

primula – diffidence

pyrethrum – I am not changed, they wrong me

rocket – rivalry

rosemary – remembrance

rue – disdain

sage – esteem, wisdom, great respect, 'I will suffer all for you'

saxifrage (mossy) affection

sorrel – affection, ill-timed wit, joy

sorrel (wood) – joy, maternal tenderness

spearmint – warm sentiment

speedwell – female fidelity

tansy – I declare war against you, resistance, life everlasting, hostile thoughts

tarragon – dragon's blood, fire, ward off serpents and dragons

thyme – activity, thriftiness, happiness, courage

valerian – an accommodating disposition

veronica – fidelity

violet – faithfulness, love, modesty

vipers bugloss – cheering

water lily – purity of heart

witch-hazel – a spell

wolfsbane (aconite) – misanthropy

wormwood – absence, do not be discouraged

yarrow – war, everlasting love

Thyme. Facing page: Speedwell.

INDEX

Anise 158
Art 157
Astragalus 168
Balsam 97
Basil 29, 154
Bay leaf 38
Belladonna 150, 157, 158
Berberis 168
Bloodroot 168
Borage 98, 154, 158
Burdock 134
Butcher's broom 168
Calendula 86, 158
Cat's claw 168
Centaury 106
Chamomile 121, 159
Chaparral 168
Chervil 158
Chicory 104
Chives 34, 158
Clover 122
Coriander 33
Cowslip 76, 156
Curcumin 168
Daisy, Ox-eye 80
Dandelion 118
Dang Shen root 168
Deadly nightshade 150, 155, 157, 158
Dill 40, 154, 155
Dock 128
Doctrine of Signatures 11
Echinacea 168
Evening primrose 133,
Fennel 49, 50, 156
Feverfew 125, 169
Field poppy 57
Flax 110, 155
Foxglove 61, 156

Garlic 22, 154, 155, 159
Gentian 101
Ginger 169
Goldenrod 89, 159
Goldenseal 168
Henbane 168
Herb specifics 158
Hibiscus 90
Honeysuckle 62, 156
Iris 69, 157
Ivy 142, 156, 160
Juice therapy 168
Laurel 38
Lavender 70, 160–1
Lemon balm 46
Linseed see Flax
Liverwort 145
Love 154
Lungwort 146
Magic 155–57
Mallow 82, 161
Mangosteen 170
Marigold 86, 154
Marjoram 42, 154
Marriage 154
Marshmallow 82, 161
Meadow cranesbill 65
Meadowsweet 137
Milk thistle 138
Mint 18, 161
Mistletoe 170
Morning glory 74
Mushrooms 170
Music 157
Myrtle 93, 154
Nasturtium 66
Nettle 126, 156, 161
Opium poppy 58
Orchid 78

Oregano 45, 162
Orris root 69, 157
Ox-eye daisy 80
Parsley 20, 162
Pau D'Arco 170
Peas 154
Pheasant's eye 113
Poppies 57–59, 157, 162
Pot marigold 86
Primula (primrose) 54, 156
Pyrethrum 94
Red clover 170
Rocket 37
Rosemary 25, 155, 157, 162–3
Sage 30, 157
Sheep sorrel 170
Skullcap 170
Sorrel 129
Speedwell 102, 156
St John's wort 156
Sutherlandia 170
Sweet violet 73
Tansy 114
Tarragon 50, 163
Thorowax (Hare's ear) 171
Thyme 26, 154, 157, 163
Valerian 141
Venus flytrap 171
Violet 73, 156, 164, 171
Viper's bugloss 109
Walnuts 171
Water lily 85, 154
Wheatgrass 171
Wild marjoram 45, 162
Witchcraft 155
Witch-hazel 130
Wolfsbane (aconite) 149
Wormwood 171

IMAGE CREDITS

The author and publisher gratefully acknowledge the permission granted to reproduce the copyright material in this book. Every effort has been made to trace copyright holders and to obtain their permission for the use of illustrative material. The publisher apologizes for any errors or omissions in the credit list and would be grateful to be notified of any corrections that should be incorporated in future reprints or editions of this book.

ACKNOWLEDGEMENTS

Grateful thanks to all the Worth Press team for their amazing support.

BIBLIOGRAPHY

Allen, Gary: *Herbs, A Global History* The Edible Series, Reaktion Books Ltd (2012)
Bown, Deni: *RHS Encyclopedia of Herbs and their Uses* Dorling Kindersley Ltd (1995)
Culpeper, Nicholas: *The British Herbal and Family Physician* Milner and Company Ltd
Day, Liz: *Herb and Spice Guide: Fascinating Facts and Delicious Recipes* Schwartz (2009)
Fortt, William: *The Little Book of Herb Tips* Absolute Press (2006)
Pratt, Anne: *Wild Flowers (Volumes 1 and II)* Society for Promoting Christian Knowledge (1857)
Botanical.com, A Modern Herbal by Mrs. M Grieve
Herb Facts (herbfacts.co.uk)
Fun Flower Facts (pinterest.com)